STATES OF MATTER

By the Same Author

THE KINETICS OF REACTIONS IN SOLUTIONS
Oxford University Press: 1933
Second edition: 1947

PHYSICAL CHEMISTRY: AN INTRODUCTION
Cambridge University Press: 1940
Reprinted: 1947
Reprinted with corrections: 1951

STATES OF MATTER

E. A. MOELWYN-HUGHES

Lecturer in Physical Chemistry University of Cambridge

OLIVER AND BOYD

EDINBURGH AND LONDON

NEW YORK: INTERSCIENCE PUBLISHERS INC.

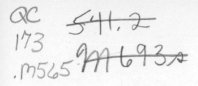

OLIVER AND BOYD LTD
Tweeddale Court
Edinburgh 1

39a Welbeck Street
London, W. 1

FIRST PUBLISHED 1961

Printed in Great Britain by
Oliver and Boyd Ltd., Edinburgh

PREFACE

THIS book is based on a course of eight lectures recently delivered at the University of Cambridge. Its object is to give a brief account of some scientific conceptions currently held on the principal states of matter, unified by the concept of intermolecular forces, which appears to me to be the only principle capable of giving them coherence. This concept I have applied as directly and in as simple a form as possible. In writing the book as in preparing the lectures I had in mind not so much the specialist in any of the states of matter as the general scientist who is interested in them all.

CHEMICAL LABORATORIES
LENSFIELD ROAD, CAMBRIDGE
1961

CONTENTS

I

GENERAL THEORY

THE stable, or equilibrium, state of a system may be defined in many ways. Mathematically, it is the state of maximum probability; thermodynamically, it is the state of minimum free energy; experimentally, it is the state from which the system exhibits no tendency to depart. Glasses and subcooled liquids in metastable states from which they are continuously, though only slowly, changing, are excluded from this discussion. So also are systems containing radioactive elements, for these are notoriously unstable. It follows from the thermodynamic definition of stability that all the forces acting on all the molecules in a stable system must balance. These forces may consist of (1) internal interactions, i.e. the mutual repulsions and attractions of molecules, and (2) external influences due to gravitational, electrical or magnetic fields or to hydrostatic pressure.

Mie's equation

Let us consider the intermolecular forces first. A general expression proposed by Mie (1903) for the interaction energy of an isolated pair of atoms or molecules at a distance a cm. apart is

$$\phi = Aa^{-n} - Ba^{-m}, \qquad \ldots\ldots\ldots 1$$

where A and B are positive constants, and n and m integers with $n > m$. The interaction energy of a pair of xenon atoms, for example, is given, in ergs, by the equation

$$\phi = \frac{5 \cdot 07 \times 10^{-95}}{a^{11}} - \frac{5 \cdot 27 \times 10^{-58}}{a^{6}}, \qquad \ldots\ldots\ldots 2$$

as is shown in Figs. 1A and 1B. The corresponding intermolecular force is

$$X = -\frac{d\phi}{da} = nAa^{-(n+1)} - mBa^{-(m+1)}. \qquad \ldots\ldots\ldots 3$$

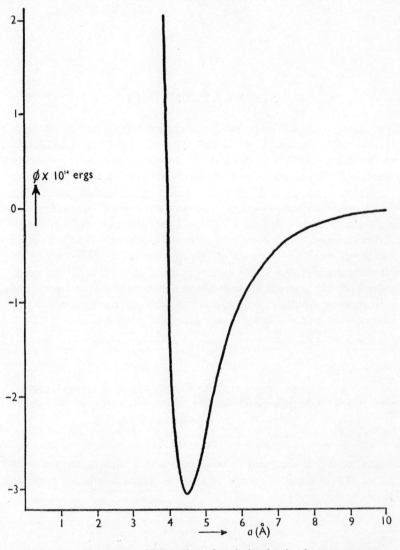

FIG. 1A. The energy of interaction of an isolated pair of xenon atoms
as a function of their distance apart.

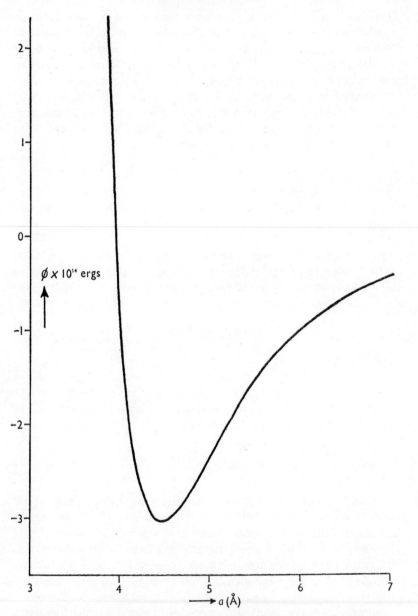

FIG. 1B. The energy of interaction of an isolated pair of xenon atoms as a function of their distance apart, with the interatomic distance shown on a magnified scale.

It will be observed that the first term represents a positive force, or a repulsion, and the second term a negative force, or an attraction. Neither force depends on an angle, and each is therefore said to be spherically symmetrical. More is known about the forces of attraction, especially those of electrostatic origin, and exact expressions can often be ascribed to B and m. That forces of repulsion should, like many forces of attraction, obey an inverse power law is largely an assumption. Some theorists prefer an exponential dependence, but experimentalists are, on the whole, satisfied with the term used here.

Specific forms of the constant B

(1) $m = 1$. The energy of interaction of two ions bearing charges e_A and e_B at a distance a apart is given by Coulomb's law as $e_A e_B/a$. If the valencies are denoted, in sign and magnitude, by z_A and z_B, we may express the energy in terms of the protonic charge ($\varepsilon = 4\cdot 802 \times 10^{-10}$ e.s.u.) as $z_A z_B \varepsilon^2$. The term B in such systems can be positive or negative, according to the signs of the changes. By including the term representing the intrinsic repulsion, we have, for a pair of ions.

$$\phi = Aa^{-n} + \frac{e_A e_B}{a}$$

$$= Aa^{-n} + \frac{z_A z_B \varepsilon^2}{a}. \qquad \ldots\ldots\ldots 4$$

Only when z_A and z_B have opposite signs can such a system be stable. The interaction energy of a univalent cation ($z_A = +1$) and a univalent anion ($z_B = -1$), for example, is

$$\phi = Aa^{-n} - \frac{\varepsilon^2}{a}. \qquad \ldots\ldots\ldots 5$$

Such an expression provides an interpretation of the stability of inorganic crystals (Born, 1919), and, after making allowance for the influence of the solvent, for the stability of ion-pairs in solution.

(2) $m = 2$. When a point charge e_A is placed at a distance a from the centre of an electric dipole of moment μ_B, so that the line of centres is inclined at an angle θ to the polar axis (Fig. 2), there is an interaction energy of magnitude $-(e_A \mu_B \cos \theta)/a^2$. The maximum positive interaction energy for a cation is found when $\theta = \pi$, i.e. when the ion is placed along the polar axis behind the positive tail of the dipole. Of greater interest is the position of minimum interaction, which is

negative. This occurs when the positive charge, again lying in the direction of the polar axis, faces the negative end of the dipole. The intrinsic repulsion, which does not depend on the angle θ, must again be included, so that the sum of the interaction energies is

$$\phi = Aa^{-n} - \frac{e_A\mu_B \cos \theta}{a^2}. \qquad\qquad ....6$$

This equation has proved helpful in explaining the existence and in assessing the stability of solvated ions.

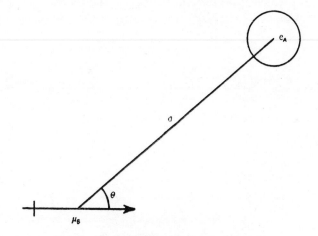

FIG. 2. The interaction between an ion and a permanent dipole.

(3) $m = 3$. Let us next consider two permanent dipoles having moments μ_A and μ_B and their centres separated by a distance, a. Provided a is large compared with the length of the dipole, the interaction energy is

$$\frac{-\mu_A\mu_B}{a^3} (2 \cos \theta_A \cos \theta_B - \sin \theta_A \sin \theta_B \cos \psi),$$

where the angles θ_A and θ_B have the meaning indicated in Fig. 3, and ψ is the angle of inclination between the planes in which the polar axes lie. The following are examples of the electrostatic component of the interaction energies of two polar molecules lying in the same plane ($\phi = 0$):

θ_A	θ_B	Orientation	Interaction energy
0	0	↦ ↦	$-2\mu_A\mu_B/a^3$
0	π	↦ ↤	$+2\mu_A\mu_B/a^3$
0	$\pi/2$	↦ ↕	0
$\pi/2$	$\pi/2$	↕ ↕	$+\mu_A\mu_B/a^3$
$\pi/2$	$3\pi/2$	↕ ↕	$-\mu_A\mu_B/a^3$

The important positions are the first and last in the list, for these allow a negative electrostatic energy. The interaction between permanent dipoles contributes to the deviations of gases and solutions

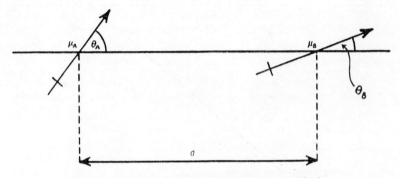

FIG. 3. The interaction between two permanent dipoles.

from normal behaviour. When one of the dipoles terminates in a hydrogen atom, the bond it forms with another dipole is termed a hydrogen bond (Latimer, 1920). The origin of this bond, at one time attributed to resonance, is now recognised as electrostatic. The mutual attractions of four dipoles in one plane account satisfactorily, with a term Aa^{-n}, for the stability of the dimers, or double molecules, of the carboxylic acids in solution and in the gaseous phase.

(4) $m = 4$. The electrostatic energy of an atom or molecule of polarisability α_A within electrical field of strength F is $-(\frac{1}{2})\alpha F^2$. If the field is that due to an ion of charge z_B, then by Coulomb's law $F_B = z_B\varepsilon/a^2$, and the interaction energy is $-(\frac{1}{2})\alpha_B(z_B\varepsilon)^2/a^4$. This induction energy is one that must be superimposed on to the direct electrostatic energy when ion-dipole pairs are considered in greater detail.

(5) $m = 6$. There are three instances where the attractive energy varies inversely as the sixth power of the separation. The first is the electrostatic energy mutually induced between a pair of freely rotating dipoles. The induction energy, as before, is $-(\frac{1}{2})\alpha F^2$, but the field now is that due to the dipoles. When these are free to rotate, the average value of the square of the field exerted at a distance a from the centre of a dipole of moment μ is $\overline{F^2} = 2\mu^2/a^6$; hence the average induction energy between a dissimilar pair of freely rotating dipoles of polarisability α_A and α_B, possessing electric moments μ_A and μ_B is $-\alpha_A\mu_B^2/a^6 - \alpha_B\mu_A^2/a^6$. Between identical molecules, it is $-2\alpha\mu^2/a^6$. The second, and much more important attraction energy with $m = 6$ is that due to the coupling of electronic oscillators. The expression derived by London (1930) for it is $B = (\frac{3}{4})h\nu_i\alpha^2$, where $h\nu_i$ is the ionisation potential, and α the polarisability. Slater and Kirkwood (1931) have modified the equation to $B = (\frac{3}{4})\sqrt{Z}h\nu_e\alpha^2$, where Z is the number of electrons in the outermost shell of each atom or molecule, and ν_e is the mean electronic vibration frequency.

Compared with London's energy term, that due to the mutual induction is generally negligible. Between non-polar molecules, it is absent, and London's dispersion energy remains as the only one capable of explaining the mutual attraction of non-polar molecules such as helium, hydrogen, carbon dioxide and methane.

The third instance of an attraction energy varying inversely as the sixth power of the molecular separation is discussed in Chapter III.

An alternative form of Mie's equation

When the force exerted between the molecules is zero, the pair is at its equilibrium separation, a_e, which is given by equation 3 as

$$a_e^{n-m} = \frac{nA}{mB}. \qquad \ldots\ldots 7$$

By eliminating A and B in turn, we can express ϕ as follows:

$$\phi = Ba_e^{-m}\left[\frac{m}{n}\left(\frac{a_e}{a}\right)^n - \left(\frac{a_e}{a}\right)^m\right] = Aa_e^{-n}\left[\left(\frac{a_e}{a}\right)^n - \frac{n}{m}\left(\frac{a_e}{a}\right)^m\right]. \qquad \ldots\ldots 8$$

These provide two expressions for the minimum potential energy ϕ_e of the pair in its equilibrium state, namely

$$\phi_e = Ba_e^{-m}\left(\frac{m}{n} - 1\right) = Aa_e^{-n}\left(1 - \frac{n}{m}\right). \qquad \ldots\ldots 9$$

On combining with the original equation, we can now write

$$\phi = \phi_e \left(\frac{1}{m-n} \right) \left[m \left(\frac{a_e}{a} \right)^n - n \left(\frac{a_e}{a} \right)^m \right]. \qquad \ldots\ldots\ldots 10$$

This expression is simply a reformulation of Mie's original equation, representing ϕ as a function of a, but using ϕ_e and a_e as constants instead of A and B. Fig. 1, for example, is reproduced by equation 10, with $\phi_e = -3\cdot045 \times 10^{-14}$ erg, and $a_e = 4\cdot46 \times 10^{-8}$ cm.

Harmonic oscillations of an isolated pair

The gain in potential energy attending a change in the separation from a_e to a is evidently

$$\phi - \phi_e = \phi_e \left(\frac{1}{m-n} \right) \left\{ m \left[\left(\frac{a_e}{a} \right)^n - 1 \right] - n \left[\left(\frac{a_e}{a} \right)^m - 1 \right] \right\}.$$

If we denote by x the function $(a-a_e)/a_e$, we see that $a_e/a = (1+x)^{-1}$. Let us also denote by D_e the energy of dissociation,

$$D_e = \phi_{a=\infty} - \phi_{a=a_e} = -\phi_e.$$

Then

$$\phi - \phi_e = \frac{D_e}{(n-m)} \left\{ n[1-(1+x)^{-m}] - m[1-(1+x)^{-n}] \right\}.$$

On expanding by means of the binomial theorem as far as 3 terms, we obtain, for the gain in energy attending small displacements from the equilibrium state

$$\phi - \phi_e = (\tfrac{1}{2}) D_e mn \, x^2 = \tfrac{1}{2} \frac{D_e mn}{a_e^2} (a-a_e)^2.$$

The resulting motion is thus a simple harmonic one, with frequency

$$v_e = \frac{1}{2\pi a_e} \left(\frac{mnD_e}{\mu} \right)^{\frac{1}{2}}, \qquad \ldots\ldots\ldots 11$$

where μ is the reduced mass (Sutherland, 1938).

Some simple numerical applications

In order to appreciate the order of magnitude of intermolecular energies and the relative values of internuclear distances in systems of widely different character, we shall examine pairs of various particles between which a repulsion energy of the general form Aa^{-9} is assumed to prevail. The repulsion we shall regard as exerted by the complete set of 8 electrons in the L shell, i.e. as that exerted between a pair of neon atoms, taking A as 3.95×10^{-82} erg-cm.^{9}. The various attractions shall have different characters, forms and magnitudes.

(i) Interactions between two ions

If the attraction is due entirely to the Coulombic force exerted between a unit positive charge ε on one of the particles and a unit negative charge $-\varepsilon$ on the other, the total interaction energy may be expressed as follows:

$$\phi = \frac{3.95 \times 10^{-82}}{a^9} - \frac{\varepsilon^2}{a}. \qquad \dots\dots\dots 12$$

On using the condition of minimum energy, we find in this instance that

$$a_e = 1.88 \text{ Å};$$
$$D_e = 1.09 \times 10^{-11} \text{ erg/pair} = 157 \text{ kilocal./g. mole}.$$

The pair thus contemplated must resemble a molecule of sodium fluoride in the gas phase, for which Verwey and de Boer (1936) find $a_e = 1.64$ Å, and $D_e = 160$ kilocal./g. mole. We may disregard the difference between the two sets of values, because, in the interests of simplicity, we have omitted certain subsidiary terms.

(ii) Interactions between an ion and a dipole

Let one of the particles retain its unit positive charge ε and let the other particle be electrically neutral, and possess a permanent electrical dipole of moment μ. In its position of minimum energy, the cation lies in the direction of the principal axis of the dipole, facing its negative end, with an interaction energy of

$$\phi = \frac{3.95 \times 10^{-82}}{a^9} - \frac{\varepsilon\mu}{a^2}. \qquad \dots\dots\dots 13$$

Now μ for the water molecule is 1.83×10^{-18} e.s.u. The part of the oxygen atom remote from the two hydrogen atoms resembles the neon atom sufficiently to justify the retention of the same repulsion constant. With these values, we find

$$a_e = 2.14 \text{ Å};$$
$$D_e = 1.50 \times 10^{-12} \text{ erg/pair} = 21.6 \text{ kilocal./g. mole}.$$

B

The experimental value of the energy required to liberate one gram equivalent of sodium and fluoride ions from dilute aqueous solution is approximately 218 kilocals. About 10 ion-dipole bonds of the type here considered would thus appear to be broken in the process. Of these, 4 probably refer to the cation, and 6 to the anion.

(iii) *Interactions between two dipoles*

If the same repulsion constant still holds, the energy of interaction of two water molecules in their most favourable orientation is

$$\phi = \frac{3 \cdot 95 \times 10^{-82}}{a^9} - \frac{2\mu^2}{a^3}. \qquad \ldots\ldots\ldots 14$$

The conditions for a minimum energy lead to the following values:

$$a_e = 2 \cdot 37 \text{ Å};$$
$$D_e = 3 \cdot 36 \times 10^{-13} \text{ erg} = 4 \cdot 84 \text{ kilocal.}$$

This interaction energy is the principal component of the so-called hydrogen bond. If liquid water forms a diamond lattice two such bonds are, on an average, broken for each water molecule that evaporates. The contribution of 9·68 kilocalories thus represents a high percentage of the total heat of vaporisation (12·86) at the absolute zero of temperature. Because of the omission of other terms, the actual percentage is probably not so high, nor the internuclear distance so small.

(iv) *Interactions between coupled electronic oscillators*

The only energy of attraction of any importance exerted between a pair of neon atoms is that due to London's dispersion effect. Using a slight modification of his expression for B we may write

$$\phi = \frac{3 \cdot 95 \times 10^{-82}}{a^9} - \frac{(Z/2)h\nu_e\alpha_o^2}{a^6}. \qquad \ldots\ldots\ldots 15$$

Here, Z, the number of electrons in the L shell, is 8; ν_e, the average frequency of electronic oscillation, is $4 \cdot 032 \times 10^{-15}$ sec.$^{-1}$; and α_o, the polarisability towards light of infinite wave length, is $3 \cdot 925 \times 10^{-25}$ c.c./atom. The coefficient of a^{-6} in equation 15 is thus $1 \cdot 65 \times 10^{-59}$ erg. cm.^{6}, and

$$a_e = 3 \cdot 30 \text{ Å};$$
$$D_e = 4 \cdot 26 \times 10^{-15} \text{ erg.} = 0 \cdot 0613 \text{ kilocal./mole.}$$

Although the equilibrium separations in these various pairs do not differ by a factor of 2, it is seen from the following summary that their energies in the equilibrium states differ by a factor of several thousands.

TABLE 1

Summary of stability conditions for various attractions and a common repulsion

Interacting pair		Type of attraction	Equilibrium separation (Å)	Energy of interaction (kilocalories/mole)
Na⁺	F⁻	Ion-ion	1·88	157
Na⁺	OH₂	Ion-dipole	2·14	21·6
OH₂	OH₂	Dipole-dipole	2·37	4·84
Ne	Ne	Coupled electronic oscillators	3·30	0·0613

Partition functions and their relation to thermodynamic functions

An understanding of the interaction energy of isolated pairs of atoms, ions or molecules is a necessary preliminary to the treatment of systems which contain a very large number of particles, and a still larger number of interactions. Methods of dealing with such systems are illustrated in later chapters. We must here recall some of the limitations of classical dynamics, and in particular its implication that momenta and energy can vary continuously. According to the quantum theory, particles can acquire energy only by discrete amounts, and can exist only in certain states that are restricted to constant energy levels. In any system composed of chemically identical atoms or molecules, the energy possessed by any one can have only the definite values ε_1, or ε_2 or ε_3, and so on. By spectroscopic means, the precise values of these energies can often be found, especially in systems of simple molecules. Generally, however, what is measured during the examination of a system is the average energy $\bar{\varepsilon}$ per particle, and quantal statistics must in general be employed to relate ε_1, ε_2, ε_3... with $\bar{\varepsilon}$. The most direct link between the discrete energies of the various particles and the average energy is provided by the molecular partition function, f, which is a summation of Boltzmann factors defined as follows in terms of the absolute temperature T, and Boltzmann's constant, k ($1\cdot3803 \times 10^{-16}$ erg/molecule-degree):

$$f = e^{-\varepsilon_1/kT} + e^{-\varepsilon_2/kT} + e^{-\varepsilon_3/kT} + \ldots = \sum_0^\infty e^{-\varepsilon_i/kT}. \qquad \ldots\ldots\ldots 16$$

It can then be readily shown that the Helmholtz free energy, A, and the total energy, E, of a system containing N chemically identical particles are

$$A = -NkT \ln f, \qquad \qquad \text{........17}$$

and $$E = NkT^2(d \ln f/dT)_V. \qquad \qquad \text{........18}$$

From the thermodynamic equation $A = E - TS$, the expression for the entropy follows:

$$S = Nk[\ln f + T(d \ln f/dT)_V]. \qquad \qquad \text{........19}$$

Expressions for other thermodynamic variables are readily obtained from these basic equations. The pressure, for example, is

$$P = -(dA/dV)_T = NkT(d \ln f/dV)_T, \qquad \text{........20}$$

and the chemical potential is

$$\mu = (dA/dN)_{T, V} = -kT[\ln f + (d \ln f/d \ln N)_{T, V}]. \qquad \text{........21}$$

II

THE CRYSTALLINE STATE

A CASUAL glance at any crystal, such as diamond or common salt, suggests that it has been built on a simple and beautiful pattern. The scientific verification of this aesthetic judgment derives from the application of Bragg's law ($2d \sin \theta = n\lambda$; $n = 1, 2, 3, \ldots$) to the reflection of X-rays which have impinged at a glancing angle θ on the facets of crystals bearing atoms in planes at a distance d apart. λ is the wavelength of the rays, and n is an integer. Strongest reflections occur when $n = 1$. Reflections from different facets of a given crystal show that d varies according to the crystallographic axes about which the crystal is suspended. By the logical use of this equation the patterns formed by atoms in various crystals have been unveiled.

Some cubic lattices

Atoms of the inert elements, with the exception of helium, and of many metals, including copper, silver, gold, calcium, strontium, aluminium, lead, barium, palladium, iridium and platinum, have been found to arrange themselves as shown in Fig. 4. The large cube is the crystal's basic unit. It contains the substance of four atoms, namely one-eighth each of the eight atoms at the corners, and one-half each of the atoms at the centres of the six faces. In terms of the distance, a, between neighbouring atoms, the atomic volume is consequently $(1/\sqrt{2})a^3$. The arrangement is known as the face-centred lattice.

The alkali metals (lithium, sodium, potassium, rubidium and caesium), as well as barium, vanadium, tantallum, molybdenum and tungsten also crystallise in a cubic lattice, but of a different kind. Here each corner of the large cube is occupied, as before, but the face centres are now empty, while an atom occupies the centre of the large cube. The pattern is known as the body-centred lattice. The arrangement is less economical, as each large cube now contains the substance of only two atoms. The atomic volume, in terms of the interatomic distance, is now $(4/3\sqrt{3})a^3$.

Experiment shows that a few elements and many compounds crystallise in modified forms of the face-centred cubic lattice. The large cube in Fig. 4 consists of eight small cubes. If, into this lattice, an atom is placed at the centre of each alternate small cube, we have the diamond lattice, in which each atom occupies the centre of a regular tetrahedron, and is surrounded by 4 atoms at the apices.

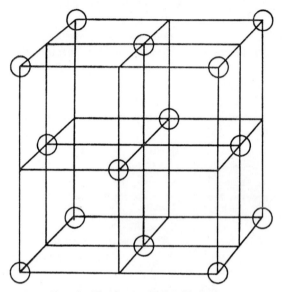

FIG. 4. The face-centred cubic lattice.

Silicon, germanium and grey tin crystallise in this way. When, into the same original face-centred cell shown in Fig. 4, atoms B differing from atoms A already present are inserted into the centre of each small cube, we have a compound of composition A_4B_8. The structure is known as the fluorspar lattice (CaF_2) in which Li_2O, Li_2S, PbF_2 and UO_2 crystallise. Finally, when all the empty lattice sites in Fig. 4 are occupied by atoms of type B, we have a compound of composition AB, and the simplest of all lattices—the rock salt lattice. Most of the alkali halides crystallise in this way.

The treatment of crystals formed from spherical, uncharged, non-polar molecules

If the energy of interaction between an isolated pair of atoms or molecules which exert spherically symmetrical forces on each other is $\phi = A/a^n - B/a^m$, the energy of interaction of one molecule with its c equidistant neighbours is $c(A/a^n - B/a^m)$. Molecules outside the c which form the first shell also exert repulsions and attractions on the central molecule, and their effect can be quantitatively allowed for when once the crystalline configuration is known. The total energy of interaction of the central molecule with all the other molecules in the system can then be expressed as $\psi = c(s_n A/a^n - s_m B/a^m)$, where s_n and s_m are pure numbers, such as those given in Table 2 (Lennard-Jones and Ingham, 1925).

TABLE 2

Summation constants (s_n and s_m) for certain cubic lattices

Lattice type n or m	Rock salt $(c = 6)$	Body-centred cubic $(c = 8)$	Face-centred cubic $(c = 12)$
6	1·4003	1·5317	1·2045
9	1·1048	1·2368	1·0410
12	1·0337	1·1394	1·0110
15	1·0115	1·0854	1·0033

The total energy of a system containing N such molecules is $U = (\frac{1}{2})N\psi$, and the average potential energy per molecule in the system is

$$u = \tfrac{1}{2}c(s_n A a^{-n} - s_m B a^{-m}). \qquad \ldots\ldots\ldots 22$$

On applying the equilibrium condition $-(du/da) = 0$ when $a = a_o$, we obtain a set of relationships closely analogous to those derived for isolated pairs. The first resembles equation 7:

$$a_o^{n-m} = s_n n A / s_m m B. \qquad \ldots\ldots\ldots 23$$

If there were no significant interactions other than those between nearest neighbours, s_n and s_m would both be unity, and a_o, the equilibrium separation in the crystal, would be the same as that in the isolated pair. As things are, s_m is greater than s_n, so that a_o is always less than a_e. From the next two equations, which resemble equation 9,

$$u_o = \tfrac{1}{2}cs_m B a_o^{-m}\left(\frac{m}{n} - 1\right) = \tfrac{1}{2}cs_n A a_o^{-n}\left(1 - \frac{n}{m}\right), \qquad \ldots\ldots\ldots 24$$

we can eliminate A and B, and obtain for the average potential energy per molecule an expression of the same form as equation 10, namely,

$$u = \frac{u_o}{m-n}\left[m\left(\frac{a_o}{a}\right)^n - n\left(\frac{a_o}{a}\right)^m \right].$$ 25

It is readily shown that the average vibration frequency of a molecule of reduced mass μ in such a system is

$$v = \frac{1}{2\pi a}\left\{ \frac{2mnu_o}{3(m-n)\mu}\left[(n-1)\left(\frac{a_o}{a}\right)^n - (m-1)\left(\frac{a_o}{a}\right)^m \right] \right\}^{\frac{1}{2}}.$$ 26

In its most stable state, the frequency is clearly

$$v_o = \frac{1}{2\pi a_o}\left[\frac{2mn\,|-u_o|}{3\mu} \right]^{\frac{1}{2}}.$$ 27

A comparison of these equations with those derived for the isolated pair shows that

$$\left(\frac{a_e}{a_o}\right)^{n-m} = \frac{s_m}{s_n},$$ 28

$$\frac{u_o}{\phi_e} = \tfrac{1}{2}c\,\frac{s_m^{n/(n-m)}}{s_n^{m/(n-m)}},$$ 29

and

$$\left(\frac{v_o}{v_e}\right)^2 = \frac{c}{6}\frac{s_m^{(n+2)/(n-m)}}{s_n^{(m+2)/(n-m)}}.$$ 30

The minimum potential energy u_o is that which, on an average, the molecule would have at the absolute zero of temperature if all the molecules in the system were at rest. The heat of sublimation of such a molecule would be $\lambda_{cr} = -u_o$. Even at the absolute zero of temperature, however, each molecule retains a vibrational energy of $(3/2)hv_o$, so that the observed latent heat of sublimation at $T = 0$ is

$$\lambda_o = \lambda_{cr} - (3/2)hv_o,$$ 31

or, if we prefer to use the maximum vibration frequency v_m, which is $(4/3)v_o$,

$$\lambda_o = \lambda_{cr} - (9/8)hv_m.$$ 32

The relationship between the terms in the equation

$$-u_o = \lambda_{cr} = \lambda_o + (3/2)hv_o$$ 33

is illustrated in Fig. 5.

Numerical application to crystalline neon

Let us derive, by means of these equations, some of the properties of crystalline neon, basing the computations on the interatomic potential

$$\phi(\text{erg}) = \frac{3 \cdot 95 \times 10^{-82}}{a^9} - \frac{1 \cdot 65 \times 10^{-59}}{a^6}. \qquad \ldots\ldots\ldots 34$$

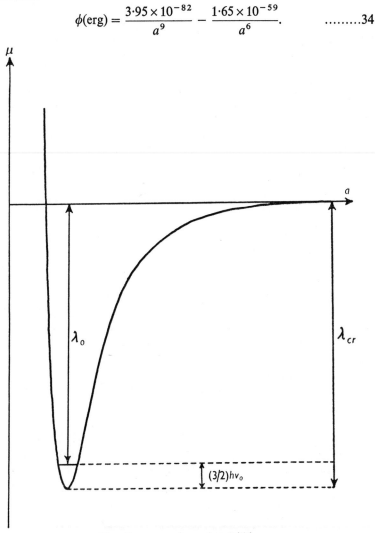

FIG. 5. $-u_o = \lambda_{\text{cr}} = \lambda_o + (3/2)h\nu_o$.

The second numerical term and the integer 6 are provided by London's theory. The first numerical term and the integer 9 may be regarded as having been evaluated by Lennard-Jones (1924), from the virial coefficients of gaseous neon in the critical region. We obtain directly for the isolated pair of atoms in its state of lowest energy the constants $a_e = 3\cdot30$ Å and $D_e = 4\cdot26 \times 10^{-15}$ erg.

Neon, as stated, crystallises in the face-centred cubic lattice. The co-ordination number, c, is thus 12. From Table 2, s_m is seen to be $1\cdot2045$, and s_n $1\cdot0410$. It follows from equation 28 that the calculated value of a_0 is $3\cdot14$ Å and of the length of the cell edge, l_0, is $4\cdot44$ Å. The observed values are $3\cdot10$ Å and $4\cdot38$ Å. Having regard to the difficulty of extrapolating densities to the absolute zero of temperature (see Dobbs and Jones, 1956), the agreement may be regarded as satisfactory.

We have next to calculate the frequency of vibration of the isolated pair, using equation 11, and from it the frequency of atomic vibration in the crystal, using equation 30. We find that v_0 is $1\cdot02 \times 10^{12}$ sec^{-1}. The calculated characteristic temperature θ, defined as $\theta = (h/k)v_m = (h/k)(4/3)v_0$, is found to be $65\cdot3°$, in reasonable agreement with the value of $64°$ measured by Clusius from the cubic region of the heat capacity-temperature curve. The computed value of the residual energy is clearly $(9/8)R\theta = (3/2)N_0hv_0 = 146$ calories/gram-atom.

Finally, from equation 29, the minimum potential energy of an atom in the crystal is found to be -593 calories. The energy required to remove a gram-atom from the crystal in its hypothetically motionless state to the infinitely dilute gaseous state is therefore $+593$ calories. After subtracting the residual energy (see Fig. 5) we calculate that the heat of sublimation at the absolute zero of temperature should be $\lambda_0 = 593 - 146 = 447$ calories/gram-atom. The value observed by Clusius is 448.

The statistical theory of monatomic solids

Einstein (1907) treated a crystal of N identical atoms as a system in which each atom vibrates harmonically with an average frequency, v, in three dimensions. According to the quantum theory, such an oscillator is restricted to the vibrational energy levels $(1/2)hv, (3/2)hv, ...,$ or in general $(v+1/2)hv$, where $v = 0, 1, 2, ...,$ and h is Planck's constant $(6\cdot624 \times 10^{-27}$ erg-sec.). Its partition function, derived from equation 16, is

$$f = [2 \sinh (hv/2kT)]^{-3}, \qquad \qquad ....35$$

and, from the general expression, 18, for the average energy, the heat capacity per gram-atom at constant volume is

$$C_V = \left(\frac{dE}{dT}\right)_V = 3R\left(\frac{h\nu}{2kT}\,\text{cosech}\,\frac{h\nu}{2kT}\right)^2. \qquad \dots\dots\dots 36$$

An experimental value for ν can be obtained from the compressibility β, the interatomic distance, a, and the structural factor κ in the expression for the atomic volume $v = \kappa a^3$:

$$\nu = \frac{1}{\pi}\left(\frac{3\kappa a}{2\mu\beta}\right)^{\frac{1}{2}}. \qquad \dots\dots\dots 37$$

The reduced mass μ of the oscillator is effectively the atomic mass. The success attending the application of these expressions to calculate the heat capacity of the diamond was rightly hailed as one of the great early triumphs of the quantum theory.

Einstein's theory explains other phenomena, equally well. For example, by equating the chemical potential of the oscillator in the crystal with that of the gaseous atom in the vapour phase at equilibrium with it, there results the vapour pressure law

$$p = \frac{(2\pi mkT)^{\frac{3}{2}}kT}{h^3}\left[2\sinh\left(\frac{h\nu}{2kT}\right)\right]^3 e^{-\lambda_0/kT} \qquad \dots\dots\dots 38$$

which has been amply verified.

In other respects, however, the theory is incomplete. It implies a permanent stability of the solid, and gives no hint of its ultimate collapse into a liquid. If we accept equation 26 as giving the vibration frequency, the isotherm of a monatomic crystal is found to be

$$\frac{Pv_o}{kT} = \frac{(h\nu/kT)}{e^{h\nu/kT}-1}\cdot\frac{1}{2}\frac{(n+2)(n-1)(a_o/a)^{n+3}-(m+2)(m-1)(a_o/a)^{m+3}}{(n-1)(a_o/a)^n-(m-1)(a_o/a)^m}$$
$$+ \frac{mnu_o}{3(m-n)kT}\left[\left(\frac{a_o}{a}\right)^{n+3}-\left(\frac{a_o}{a}\right)^{m+3}\right]. \qquad \dots\dots\dots 39$$

On using the constants of equation 2, the isotherm of solid xenon (Table 3) indicates an intermolecular separation at the melting temperature which is 2·5 per cent. greater than the observed value and a pressure at the melting temperature which is far too high (Fig. 6). While it is true that the natural pressure of the crystal is the very small excess of the kinetic pressure over the statical pressure, both of which in this instance are about 500 times as great as the difference between them, it is, nevertheless, clear that the partition function of equation 35, though adequate to account for the temperature variation of the heat capacity and vapour pressure of monatomic solids, is in other respects defective.

TABLE 3

Computed isotherm for crystalline xenon at the melting temperature

a/a_o	$v \cdot 10^{11}$ (sec^{-1})	hv/kT_m	(Pv_0/kT_m) kinetic	(Pv_0/kT_m) statical	(Pv_0/kT_m) total
1·00	8·62	0·2565	7·90	0	7·90
1·01	7·89	0·2348	7·97	−2·30	5·67
1·02	7·18	0·2135	8·10	−4·08	4·02
1·03	6·53	0·1942	8·24	−5·50	2·74
1·04	5·92	0·1760	8·45	−6·47	1·98
1·05	5·34	0·1589	8·69	−7·21	1·48
1·06	4·80	0·1429	9·01	−7·74	1·27
1·07	4·29	0·1277	9·47	−8·07	1·40
1·08	3·81	0·1131	10·28	−8·26	2·02

The ionic lattice

Born's theory of the ionic lattice (1919) historically precedes Lennard-Jones' theory of lattices formed from monatomic molecules (1924).

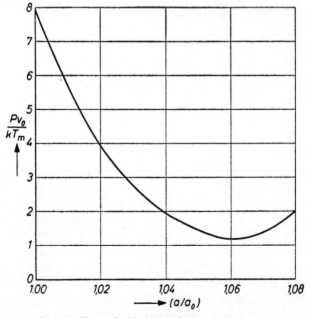

FIG. 6. Theoretical isotherm for crystalline xenon at the melting temperature.

Its basic assumption is that the units of which crystalline salts like sodium chloride are built are ions, which repel and attract one another according to Coulomb's law. The net effect of these primary electrostatic forces is an attraction. Non-electrostatic repulsions may again be represented by terms of the form Aa^{-n}. The average potential energy per molecule when the ions in a uni-univalent salt are at a distance a apart is thus

$$u = \frac{cAs_n}{a^n} - \frac{\alpha\varepsilon^2}{a}, \qquad \text{........40}$$

where ε is the electronic charge, and the second summation constant α depends, like s_n, on the lattice type. It is known as Madelung's constant. From the condition for a minimum energy ($du/da = 0$) it follows that

$$a_o^{n-1} = \frac{ncAs_n}{\alpha\varepsilon^2}, \qquad \text{........41}$$

so that in general

$$u = -\frac{\alpha\varepsilon^2}{a}\left[1 - \frac{1}{n}\left(\frac{a_o}{a}\right)^{n-1}\right], \qquad \text{........42}$$

and in particular

$$u_o = -\frac{\alpha\varepsilon^2}{a_o}\left(1 - \frac{1}{n}\right). \qquad \text{........43}$$

Experimental values of the lattice energies of the alkali halides MX have been obtained from data relating to the six steps in the Born-Haber cycle:

$$
\begin{array}{lll}
MX \text{ (cr.)} \rightarrow M \text{ (cr.)} + \tfrac{1}{2}X_2(s) & ; & \Delta H_1 = Q_f \\
M \text{ (cr.)} \rightarrow M \text{ (g.)} & ; & \Delta H_2 = L_M \\
\tfrac{1}{2}X_2(s) \rightarrow \tfrac{1}{2}X_2 \text{ (g.)} & ; & \Delta H_3 = (\tfrac{1}{2})L_{X_2} \\
M \text{ (g.)} \rightarrow M^+ \text{ (g.)} + \ominus \text{ (g.)} & ; & \Delta H_4 = V_i\varepsilon \\
\tfrac{1}{2}X_2 \text{ (g.)} \rightarrow X \text{ (g.)} & ; & \Delta H_5 = (\tfrac{1}{2})D \\
X \text{ (g.)} + \ominus \rightarrow X^- \text{ (g.)} & ; & \Delta H_6 = -E_X \\
\hline
MX \text{ (cr.)} \rightarrow M^+ \text{ (g.)} + X^- \text{ (g.)} & ; & -u_o = \overset{6}{\Sigma}\Delta H
\end{array}
$$

Here Q_f is the heat of formation of the crystalline salt from the metal and the halogen molecule in its normal state (s) at 25° C. L_M is the heat of sublimation of the metal, and L_{X_2} the molar heat of sublimation or vaporisation of the halogen. V_i is the ionisation potential of the monatomic metal and E_X the electron affinity of the monatomic halogen, both in the gas phase. D is the energy of dissociation of the halogen molecule. Some of the experimental values are given in Table 4. The integer, n, evaluated by means of equation 43, is found to increase from 7 for lithium fluoride to 16 for potassium iodide, and thus to resemble the values later found from the virial

TABLE 4

Experimental values of the lattice energies (in kilocalories per mole) of certain alkali halides

Salt	L_M	V_i	$\frac{1}{2}L_{x2}$	$\frac{1}{2}D_{x2}$	E_x	Q_f	$-U_0$
LiF	37·07	125·79	0	18·86	82·1	146·3	245·9
NaF	25·98	120·04	0	18·86	82·1	136·0	218·8
KF	21·51	101·56	0	18·86	82·1	134·5	194·3
RbF	20·51	97·79	0	18·86	82·1	131·3	186·3
LiCl	37·07	125·79	0	28·97	86·6	97·7	202·9
NaCl	25·98	120·04	0	28·97	86·6	98·2	186·6
KCl	21·51	101·56	0	28·97	86·6	104·2	169·6
RbCl	20·51	97·79	0	28·97	86·6	102·9	163·6
LiBr	37·07	125·79	3·76	22·74	80·9	83·7	192·2
NaBr	25·98	120·04	3·76	22·74	80·9	86·0	177·7
KBr	21·51	101·56	3·76	22·74	80·9	93·7	162·4
RbBr	20·51	97·79	3·76	22·74	89·9	93·0	156·9
LiI	37·07	125·79	7·42	18·05	73·2	64·8	179·9
NaI	25·98	120·04	7·42	18·05	73·2	68·8	167·1
KI	21·51	101·56	7·42	18·05	73·2	78·3	153·7
RbI	20·51	97·79	7·42	18·05	73·2	78·5	149·1

coefficients of the inert gases. The lattice energy of bi-bivalent salts is about four times as great as for uni-univalent salts at the same separation, in agreement with Born's theory.

The compressibility, β, of systems obeying Mie's potential is given by the general equation

$$\frac{1}{\beta} = -\frac{mnu_o}{9v_o},\qquad\ldots\ldots\ldots 44$$

provided the molecular volume v_o is not very different from its minimum value. For the rock-salt lattice, $m = 1$ and $v_o = 2a_o^3$, so that $1/\beta = -nu_o/18a_o^3$. The elimination of u_o provides an alternative expression for n;

$$n = 1 + \frac{18a_o^4}{\beta\alpha\varepsilon^2}.\qquad\ldots\ldots\ldots 45$$

Born found the repulsion integers given by this equation to be in reasonable agreement with his estimates from the lattice energies.

If the energy due to the coupling of electronic oscillators is included the average energy per molecule of a uni-valent salt becomes

$$u = \frac{cs_n A}{a^n} - \frac{\alpha \varepsilon^2}{a} - \frac{cs_6 B}{a^6}, \qquad \ldots\ldots\ldots 46$$

and the lattice energy is consequently greater:

$$-u_o = \frac{\alpha \varepsilon^2}{a_o}\left(1 - \frac{1}{n}\right) + \frac{cs_6 B}{a_0^6}\left(1 - \frac{6}{n}\right). \qquad \ldots\ldots\ldots 47$$

Applied to crystalline KCl, for which $-u_o = 169.6$ kilo-calories/mole, $\alpha = 1.7476$, $a_o = 3.149$ Å, $c = 6$ and $s_6 = 1.4003$, n is found to be 9·4 or 8·6, depending on whether the value of B given by the virial data (1.03×10^{-58} erg. cm.^{6}) or that given by the Slater-Kirkwood equation (1.52×10^{-58} erg. cm.^{6}) is accepted. Although the percentage of the total energy attributable to dispersion forces is found to be less than 3·5, its inclusion results in a lowering of the value of n from 13 to 9.

In a modification of the original theory, the repulsion energy Aa^{-n} has been replaced by a term proportional to $e^{-a/\rho}$, and a further contribution arising from the interaction of quadrupoles is introduced (Born and Mayer, 1932; Born and Huang, 1954). ρ is found to be about 0·35 Å for most of the alkali halides.

Salt molecules

Mie's potential, as Vervey and de Boer (1936) have shown, can be applied to molecules of salt in the vapour phase as well as to crystalline salts. For a molecule in the gas, we have, omitting polarisation and dispersion effects,

$$u_g = \frac{A}{a^n} - \frac{\varepsilon^2}{a}, \qquad \ldots\ldots\ldots 48$$

giving a molecular energy of separation of

$$-u_e = \frac{\varepsilon^2}{a_e}\left(1 - \frac{1}{n}\right). \qquad \ldots\ldots\ldots 49$$

It follows that

$$\frac{a_o}{a_e} = \left(\frac{cs_n}{\alpha}\right)^{\frac{1}{n-1}} \qquad \ldots\ldots\ldots 50$$

and that

$$\frac{u_o}{a_e} = \alpha \frac{a_e}{a_o}.$$ 51

Both conclusions have been experimentally confirmed. The computed value of a_e for KCl, for example, is 2·666 Å: the observed value is 2·6666 Å. The heat of sublimation of salt molecules

$$\lambda_o = u_e - u_o.$$ 52

calculated in this way are in satisfactory agreement with those observed by Deitz (1936) and Bradley (1953).

Defects in monatomic solids

Several facts indicate that crystals, though chemically pure, have seldom the perfect lattice arrangement suggested by the X-ray work of the pioneer investigators. Let us consider first the values of the Avogadro number, N_o, found by dividing the molar volume ($V_m = M/\rho$) of a crystal by its molecular volume ($v = \kappa a^3$). The molar weight, M, the density, ρ, and the internuclear distance a can all be measured correctly to within 1 part in 10,000. Nevertheless, values of $N_o = V_m/v$ found for different pure crystals are, except for calcite and diamond, discordant, and higher than the reputable value of N_0 derived from other sources. The explanation is that, while calcite and diamond are perfect lattices, most other crystals are slightly imperfect, in the sense that some of the lattice sites are unoccupied. This view is supported by a great wealth of evidence. Without a few empty cells in an otherwise perfect crystal, it would be difficult to explain, for example, diffusion in metals, and the relatively high electrical conductivity of crystalline salts.

Defects in crystals are of two types. If an atom leaves its regular site and finds a place for itself anywhere in the crystal other than on a regular site, the defect is said to be of the Frenkel type. The new position taken up by the miscreant is termed an intersticial site. If an atom, on leaving its regular site, forces the crystal to provide another regular site for it, the resulting defect is said to be of the Schottky type. In such a case, the general structure of the crystal is like that of the perfect crystal except that a few of the regular sites are unoccupied. Another way of describing it is to say that the crystal is regular except for the presence of a small number of holes of atomic size.

The number, N_h of holes of atomic size due to Schottky defects in a crystal consisting of N_m atoms can be estimated as follows, provided their number is so small as to make it improbable that two holes shall occupy neighbouring sites. The total number of links that can be formed between all the neighbouring sites is $\frac{1}{2}c(N_m+N_h)$, where c is the co-ordination number. Of these, cN_h links are those between atoms and empty sites, and contribute nothing to the energy. The number of atom-atom contacts is thus $\frac{1}{2}c(N_m+N_h)-cN_h = \frac{1}{2}c(N_m-N_h)$. Denoting by ϕ the interaction energy of a single pair, the sum of the near-neighbour interaction energies is $U = \frac{1}{2}c\phi(N_m-N_h)$. Let the partition function of an atom which is next to a hole be f_o, and that of an atom surrounded by other atoms be f_m. Allowing for the accessibility of all sites for the atoms, we obtain for the system a grand partition function:

$$F = \frac{(N_m+N_h)!}{N_m!\,N_h!} \cdot f_m^{(N_m-cN_h)} \cdot f_o^{cN_h} \cdot e^{-\mathcal{U}/kT}. \qquad \ldots\ldots\ldots 53$$

The most probable arrangement is that corresponding to a maximum value of F, or a minimum value of the free energy, and is obtained by equating $d \ln F/dN_h$ to zero. Then

$$\frac{N_h}{N_m+N_h} = \left(\frac{f_o}{f_m}\right)^c e^{\frac{1}{2}c\phi/kT}. \qquad \ldots\ldots\ldots 54$$

Disregarding the difference between the two atomic partition functions, and noting that, on the basis of near-neighbour interactions only, $\frac{1}{2}c\phi = -\lambda_o$, we have

$$\frac{N_h}{N_m} = \frac{1}{e^{\lambda_o/kT}-1}. \qquad \ldots\ldots\ldots 55$$

This ratio is $7\cdot9 \times 10^{-6}$ for crystalline xenon at the melting temperature, when λ_o/kT_m is $11\cdot75$. If the holes are regularly spaced, their distance apart is thus about fifty times as great as the atomic separation.

According to these estimates, the Schottky defects would make but a negligible contribution to the coefficient of expansion of a monatomic solid. Another estimate of their number can be based on the extreme view that thermal expansion is due entirely to the creation of holes of atomic size, without altering the interatomic distance. If w is the work necessary to create one hole, we would then have

$$\frac{V}{V_o} = \frac{N_m+N_h}{N_m} = \frac{1}{1-e^{-w/kT}}. \qquad \ldots\ldots\ldots 56$$

C

The ratio of the volume at the melting temperature to that at the absolute zero is $1\cdot107\pm0\cdot004$ for neon, argon, krypton and xenon. This requires w/kT_m to be 7/3, indicating a work term which is less than λ_o by a factor of about 5. The truth probably lies between these limits, and a more satisfactory theory must allow for a number of other factors, such as the distribution of the energy w between a

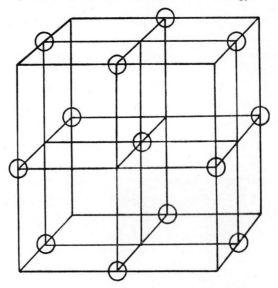

FIG. 7. The face-centred cubic lattice, as in Fig. 4, but displaced by ½ cell length.

number of oscillators, the existence of holes of various sizes, and the concurrent appearance of Frenkel defects.

Diffusion in monatomic solids

Base metals which have been plated with gold are found, after a time, to contain it at considerable depths, so that the gold atoms initially present on the surface must have penetrated into the interior of the base metals. By using radioactive isotopes, the coefficient of self diffusion of a metal can be measured at almost any temperature (Hevesy, 1920). It is defined by Fick's law as the number of molecules crossing unit area in unit time under unit concentration gradient. To derive a simple expression for it, let us again consider a unit cell of the face-centred cubic type, drawn as in Fig. 7, which is Fig. 4

displaced linearly by one-half the cell length. Let p denote the probability per second that the atom at the centre shall escape through the wall on the right-hand side into the adjoining cell, the central site of which is assumed to be unoccupied. In terms of the interatomic distance, a, the area of the wall is $2a^2$, and the concentration gradient is $1/4a^4$, so that, by Fick's first law, the coefficient of diffusion is $D = 2a^2p$. As in similar problems in chemical kinetics, the probability p may be regarded as the product of a vibration frequency v and the Boltzmann factor giving the chance that an atom shall possess an energy of at least ε in two quadratic terms. Thus

$$D = 2a^2ve^{-\varepsilon/kT}. \qquad \ldots\ldots\ldots 57$$

The order of magnitude of the term preceding the Boltzmann factor is 10^{-2} cm.^{2} sec.$^{-1}$, which, for most metals, is in agreement with experiment.

The energy of transit has been evaluated on the assumption that the energy of interaction of the migrating atom with each of its neighbours can be expressed by equation 1 with $n = 9$ and $m = 6$. The energy of interaction of the moving atom with the 20 relevant neighbours increases as it moves from the centre to the wall. If these 20 neighbour atoms were to remain at their posts, the work which would have to be done to move the atom from the centre of its cell to the centre of the wall is found to be about fifteen times as great as the heat of sublimation, λ. This represents an unsurpassable barrier. In other words, the atom is much more likely to vaporize than to diffuse. If, however, the four atoms in the plane of transit recede in that plane, the work required is greatly reduced. The lowest height of the energy barrier is then found to be about $(\frac{1}{2})\lambda$, in reasonable agreement with experiment, and occurs when the atoms in the plane of transit have receded so as to be as far from the diffusing atom as its original neighbours were.

It is thus clear that the diffusion of an atom in a solid is made possible only by the co-operation of other atoms. In its simplest terms, the result of the calculations may be summarised by saying that diffusion corresponds to a decrease in the number of neighbouring atoms at a constant separation.

III

THE GASEOUS STATE

MOLECULAR motion in gases is completely chaotic, in striking contrast to molecular motion in crystals, where molecules vibrate in an orderly fashion on a set of permanent sites. Each of the N molecules in a gas has access to the total volume V, and, under classical conditions, can have any imaginable velocity in any direction. The problem of treating the molecular interactions in such a system is naturally more complicated than the corresponding problem in solids. Nevertheless, much has been learned of intermolecular forces from experiments on gases. These aim at establishing adequate isotherms, i.e. relationships between the pressure and volume of the gas at constant temperature. They are of various forms. In the Leiden isotherms

$$\frac{PV}{NkT} = 1 + K_2 \left(\frac{N}{V}\right) + K_3 \left(\frac{N}{V}\right)^2 + \dots \qquad \dots\dots\dots 58$$

the coefficients of integral powers of the concentration, N/V, give a measure of the deviations of gaseous behaviour from the ideal. To reproduce precise data at a single temperature as many as 7 of these coefficients are sometimes needed. We shall here deal only with the second virial coefficient, K_2. It is found to be negative at low temperatures and positive at high temperatures. The particular temperature T_B at which it is zero is known as the Boyle point, and is, for many simple gases nearly three times as great as the critical temperature, T_C. More precisely,

$$T_B/T_c = 2\cdot75 = 11/4. \qquad \dots\dots\dots 59$$

Over wide reaches of temperature, K_2 is found to vary linearly with respect to the reciprocal of the absolute temperature, as may be seen from Fig. 8.

The second virial coefficient of a van der Waals gas

The van der Waals equation

$$P = \frac{NkT}{V-Nb} - \frac{N^2a}{V^2} \qquad \dots\dots\dots 60$$

28

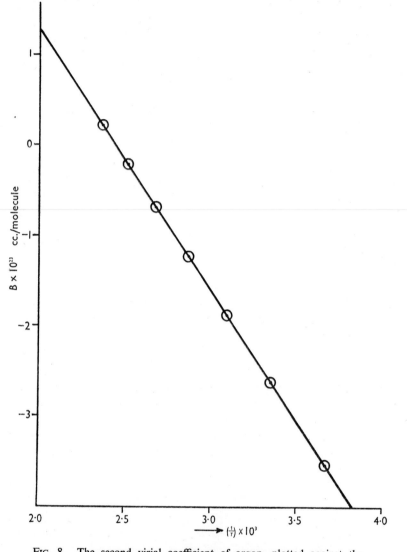

FIG. 8. The second virial coefficient of argon, plotted against the reciprocal of the absolute temperature. (Data of Michels, Wijker and Wijker, 1949).

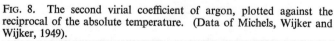

can be recast in the form of equation 1, by using the binomial theorem to expand the term $\left(1 - \dfrac{Nb}{V}\right)^{-1}$. We then find that

$$\frac{PV}{NkT} = 1 + \left(b - \frac{a}{kT}\right)\frac{N}{V} + b^2\left(\frac{N}{V}\right)^2 + \dots \qquad \dots\dots\dots 61$$

The second virial coefficient for a van der Waals gas is thus

$$K_2 = b - \frac{a}{kT}, \qquad \dots\dots\dots 62$$

and the temperature of the Boyle point is clearly $T_B = a/bk$. But, for such a gas, the temperature of the critical point is $T_c = 8a/27bk$. The ratio T_B/T_c would then be 27/8, which is too large, indicating the inadequacy of equation 60 in this respect.

Rayleigh's equation

To obtain a theoretical expression for the second virial coefficient, we begin with a general equation derived by Clausius and known as the virial theorem. According to it,

$$PV = NkT - \tfrac{1}{3}\Sigma\, a(d\phi/da). \qquad \dots\dots\dots 63$$

The force acting between a pair of molecules at a distance a apart is $-d\phi/da$. To evaluate the last term in equation 63, the product of this force and the distance must be obtained for each molecular pair, and all such products must be summed. Rayleigh bases his treatment on Boltzmann's law, which gives the concentration, n_a, of molecules at a distance a from some central molecule

$$n_a = n \cdot e^{-\phi/kT}. \qquad \dots\dots\dots 63a$$

Only at large separations when ϕ becomes zero can n_a be identified with the bulk concentration $n\,(= N/V)$. In a spherical shell of thickness da at a distance a from the central molecule, the number of molecules is $4\pi a^2 da \cdot n_a$. Each one interacts with the central molecule, contributing $a(d\phi/da)$ to the virial. The contribution to the virial due to one molecule is obtained by integrating the product $4\pi a^2 da \cdot n_a \times a(d\phi/da)$ over all values of a from zero to infinity. The total contribution due to all the N molecules in the system is $N/2$ times as great. Then

$$\Sigma a \frac{d\phi}{da} = \tfrac{1}{2}N \int_o^\infty 4\pi a^2 da \cdot n_a \cdot a \frac{d\phi}{da}$$

$$= \frac{2\pi N^2}{V} \int_o^\infty e^{-\phi/kT} a^3 d\phi.$$

Integration by parts allows us to express this result in a more convenient form:

$$\Sigma a \frac{d\phi}{da} = - \frac{6\pi N^2 kT}{V} \int_o^\infty (1 - e^{-\phi/kT}) a^2 da.$$

On substituting in equation 5, we obtain Rayleigh's result:

$$\frac{PV}{NkT} = 1 + 2\pi \left(\frac{N}{V}\right) \int_o^\infty (1 - e^{-\phi/kT}) a^2 da. \qquad \ldots\ldots\ldots 64$$

This equation, with $\phi = Aa^{-n}$ has been integrated by Jeans (1904), and with $\phi = -Ba^{-m}$ by Keesom (1912). The integration when $\phi = Aa^{-n} - Ba^{-m}$ was carried out by Lennard-Jones (1924). The resulting expressions are mathematically complicated. A still more recondite equation emerges, as Stockmayer (1948) has shown, when to Mie's potential is added that due to interacting dipoles. No attempt is made here to reproduce these exact solutions. Only an approximate treatment is given to illustrate the method.

A third convenient form of Mie's equation

We have already employed two equivalent forms of the potential energy equation proposed by Mie, and now introduce a third version, more appropriate to the present problem. We define a " diameter " or a " closest distance of approach " σ as the value of a when the potential energy of an isolated pair is zero (see Fig. 9). Then, since

$$\phi = \frac{\phi_e}{m-n} \left[m \left(\frac{a_e}{a}\right)^n - n \left(\frac{a_e}{a}\right)^m \right], \qquad \ldots\ldots\ldots 10$$

we see that σ and a_e are related to each other as follows:

$$\left(\frac{a_e}{\sigma}\right)^{n-m} = \frac{n}{m}. \qquad \ldots\ldots\ldots 65$$

After eliminating a_e and writing D_e for $-\phi_e$, we obtain the energy equation in the desired form:

$$\phi = \frac{D_e}{n-m}\left(\frac{n^n}{m^m}\right)^{\frac{1}{n-m}}\left[\left(\frac{\sigma}{a}\right)^n - \left(\frac{\sigma}{a}\right)^m\right]. \qquad \ldots\ldots\ldots66$$

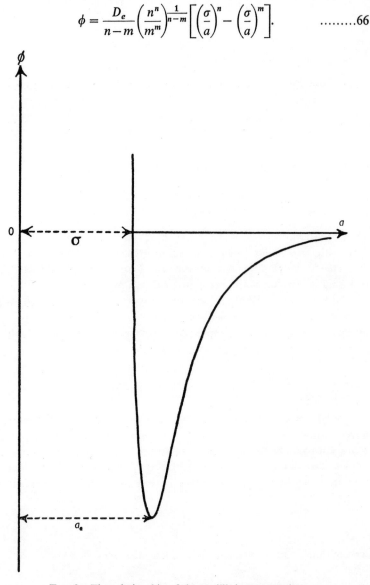

Fig. 9. The relationship of the equilibrium separation, a_e to the " closest distance of approach ", σ.

The particular form assumed when n is 12 and m 6 is extremely simple:

$$\phi = 4D_e\left[\left(\frac{\sigma}{a}\right)^{12} - \left(\frac{\sigma}{a}\right)^6\right]. \qquad \dots\dots67$$

Mie's potential when n and m have these values is often referred to as the Lennard-Jones or 12-6 potential. In general, we may write γ for $(n^n/m^m)^{\frac{1}{n-m}}$, so that

$$\phi = \frac{\gamma D_e}{n-m}\left[\left(\frac{\sigma}{a}\right)^n - \left(\frac{\sigma}{a}\right)^m\right]. \qquad \dots\dots68$$

An approximate computation of the second virial coefficient and the Boyle point in terms of intermolecular energies

The integral in equation 64 may be split in two as follows:

$$\int_o^\infty = \int_o^\sigma + \int_\sigma^\infty.$$

When a is less than σ, the interaction energy is positive, and increases rapidly as a diminishes. In this region, therefore, the term $\exp(-\phi/kT)$ may be ignored in comparison with unity, and the first part of the integral becomes $\sigma^3/3$. When a is greater than σ, ϕ is negative, and, if it is small compared with kT, we can replace $1 - e^{-\phi/kT}$ by ϕ/kT. The approximate form of Rayleigh's equation now becomes

$$\frac{PV}{NkT} = 1 + \frac{2\pi N}{V}\left[\frac{\sigma^3}{3} + \int_\sigma^\infty \frac{\phi}{kT}\cdot a^2 da\right].$$

On using equation 66, we find

$$\frac{PV}{NkT} = 1 + \frac{2\pi N}{V}\left[\frac{\sigma^3}{3} - \frac{(n^n/m^m)^{\frac{1}{n-m}}}{(n-3)(m-3)}\cdot\sigma^3\cdot\left(\frac{D_e}{kT}\right)\right]. \qquad \dots\dots69$$

The second virial coefficient is thus

$$K_2 = \tfrac{2}{3}\pi\sigma^3\left[1 - \frac{3(n^n/m^m)^{\frac{1}{n-m}}}{(n-3)(m-3)}\left(\frac{D_e}{kT}\right)\right] \qquad \dots\dots70$$

and the temperature of the Boyle point is given by the equation:

$$kT_B = \frac{3(n^n/m^m)^{\frac{1}{n-m}}}{(n-3)(m-3)}D_e. \qquad \dots\dots71$$

With $m = 6$, and $n = 12$, we have $kT_B = (8/3)D_e$, and with $m = 6$ and $n = 9$, we have $kT_B = (27/8)D_e$. Equation 59 then leads to the values

$$D_e = \left(\frac{33}{32}\right) kT_c(n = 12) \quad \text{or} \quad \left(\frac{22}{27}\right) kT_c(n = 9). \qquad \ldots\ldots\ldots 72$$

Lennard-Jones, by fitting the theoretical isotherm to the critical data, found D_e/kT_c to be approximately 3/4.

From the experimental results plotted in Fig. 8, we find that a_e for a pair of argon atoms is 3·22 Å, and that $D_e \times 10^{14}$ is 2·11 or 1·67 ergs, according as to whether we accept n as 12 or 9.

The findings of the approximate method described here are in satisfactory agreement with those of more rigorous procedures.

Interactions between permanent dipoles

The principal energy of attraction in most gases is that due to the coupling of electronic oscillators. The energy of mutual induction has not been known to exceed 4 per cent. of the total effect, and can generally be ignored. When gaseous molecules possess permanent dipoles a further energy of attraction appears, whose magnitude is determined by the balance between electrostatic forces tending to align the molecules in positions of minimum energy and thermal forces tending to disorganise the alignments and to toss the dipoles about in haphazard fashion. The potential energy of a molecule possessing a permanent dipole moment, μ, inclined at an angle θ to the direction of a field F is $-\mu F \cos \theta$. To allow for the competition described a component, f_e, must be introduced into the total partition function of the molecule:

$$f_e = \frac{kT}{\mu F} \sinh \frac{\mu F}{kT}. \qquad \ldots\ldots\ldots 73$$

According to equation 18, the electrostatic contribution to the energy is

$$\varepsilon_e = kT - \mu F \coth \frac{\mu F}{kT}. \qquad \ldots\ldots\ldots 74$$

In strong fields at low temperatures, μF is much greater than kT, and the term $\coth (\mu F/kT)$ tends to unity. Since kT under these conditions can be ignored, the electrostatic energy is effectively $-\mu F$, which is the result directly obtainable for a static dipole inclined to the field in the most favourable position. In weak fields at high temperatures, on the other hand, μF is much less than kT, and, since coth x is now nearly $(1/x)+(x/3)$,

$$\varepsilon_e = -\tfrac{1}{3}\frac{\mu^2 F^2}{kT}. \qquad \ldots\ldots75$$

Under these conditions, the dipoles may be regarded as rotating freely, and we may adopt $2\mu^2/a^6$ as the average value of the square of the field exerted by a dipole at a distance a from its centre. Hence

$$\varepsilon_e = -\tfrac{2}{3}\frac{\mu^4}{kTa^6}, \qquad \ldots\ldots76$$

which is Keesom's result. Thus the net interaction energy of freely rotating dipoles is an attraction, varying, like the dispersion energy, inversely as the sixth power of the intermolecular separation. In the vapours of highly polar molecules like water and ammonia, this attraction may equal, or even slightly exceed, that due to dispersion forces.

A more general expression for the interaction energy of two like molecules possessing permanent moments μ at a distance a apart is

$$\phi = Aa^{-n} - Ba^{-6} - \mu^2 a^{-3}(2\cos\theta_A\cos\theta_B - \sin\theta_A\sin\theta_B\cos\psi). \quad \ldots\ldots77$$

Stockmayer (1948) has integrated equation 64 with this expression for the potential. Lumbeck and Ten Seldam (1951) have fitted the resulting equation to their data on methyl fluoride, and Rowlinson (1951) has analysed the third virial coefficient of this gas in terms of the same equation. T. A. Barker and F. Smith (1960) have shown that the second virial coefficients of acetonitrile are adequately reproduced with the following constants:

$$D_e = 3{\cdot}02\times10^{-14} \text{ erg}; \quad \sigma = 4{\cdot}38\times10^{-8} \text{ cm.}; \quad \mu = 3{\cdot}98\times10^{-18} \text{ e.s.u.}$$

Dimerisation in the gas phase

The Rayleigh-Mie method is not the only one for dealing with the behaviour of polar gases in regions where they deviate from the ideal laws. The method of chemical equilibria can also be used. Hydrogen cyanide, for example, exerts a lower pressure than can be explained on the supposition that all the molecules have the formula HCN. Giauque and Ruehrwein (1939) have found that the lowering can be explained in terms of the formation of dimers $(HCN)_2$. Clusius (1959) has treated gaseous nitric oxide in the same way. With carboxylic acids also, allowance for dimerisation is known to be sufficient, but corrections allowing for the existence of higher polymers appear to be necessary in attempting to explain the behaviour of hydroxylic compounds. The Giauque-Clusius approach to the problem has much to commend it on chemical grounds. Expressions have been given for the isotherms of gases which are partially dimerised and at the same time suffer gas imperfection as the term is ordinarily understood.

Other properties of gases

From the experimental isotherms of any gas, its free energy may be readily evaluated; and from the free energy, in turn, its heat content, entropy and heat capacity may be found. Michels and his collaborators have published detailed tables of these properties for numerous gases. Many of the properties computed from the isotherms can also be measured directly. The heat capacity at constant volume, in particular, has been determined for carbon dioxide and certain other gases by both methods. Michels finds it to vary with the volume in such a way that, at most temperatures, it passes through a maximum when the density of the gas coincides with the critical density.

Viscosity is another property of gases which has been intensively examined in the light of intermolecular forces. The theory developed by Hirschfelder, Bird and Spotz (1948) leads to an equation of the form

$$\eta = \text{constant} \times (mT)^{\frac{1}{2}} \sigma^{-2} f(kT/D_e), \qquad \ldots\ldots\ldots 78$$

where m is the mass, σ and D_e have their usual meaning, and $f(kT/D_e)$ is a complicated function which has been evaluated numerically for the Lennard-Jones or 12-6 potential. When fitted to the experimental viscosity of argon, the equation yields intermolecular energy constants in agreement with those found by other means (Table 5). The viscosity of mercury vapour at temperatures between 500° and 900° K has been examined by Epstein and Powers (1953) who conclude that, assuming m to be 6, the most probable value of n is 9. They find for mercury the constants $D_e = 11 \cdot 7 \times 10^{-14}$ erg and $a_e = 3 \cdot 25$ Å. Both these values and that of the repulsion integer agree well with the inter-molecular energy constants derived from certain properties of liquid mercury, which are $D_e = 11 \cdot 0 \times 10^{-14}$ erg, and $a_e = 3 \cdot 38$ Å. Numer-ous other methods used to determine the intermolecular constants of mercury have been critically reviewed by Epstein and Powers from whose publication Fig. 10 is reproduced.

TABLE 5

Intermolecular energy constants for argon, obtained by various methods

Method	Investigator	$D_e \times 10^{14}$(erg)	a_e(Å)
Virial coefficients	Lennard-Jones (1937)	1·65	3·82
Viscosity	Hirschfelder, Bird and Spotz (1949)	1·71	3·83
X-ray scattering	Kerr and Lund (1951)	1·62	3·80

Gas mixtures

In the theoretical study of a mixture of two gases which do not react chemically with each other, intermolecular force constants are required for three molecular pairs, so as to express the intermolecular

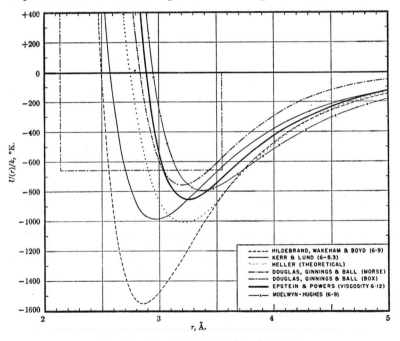

FIG. 10. The potential function of mercury.

Reproduced by permission of the American Chemical Society from L. F. Epstein and M. D. Powers' article in *The Journal of Physical Chemistry*, Vol. 57, 339, (1953).

potentials ϕ_{11}, ϕ_{22} and ϕ_{12} as functions of the molecular separations. In principle the first two sets of constants can be found from the virial coefficients B_{11} and B_{22} of the pure gases, and the third set by the following analysis of the virial coefficient of the mixture.

Equation 69, in the special case when $n = 9$ and $m = 6$, takes the form

$$\frac{PV}{NkT} = 1 + \frac{2\pi N\sigma^3}{3V}\left(1 - \frac{27}{8}\frac{D_e}{kT}\right). \qquad \ldots\ldots\ldots 79$$

The second virial coefficient, here denoted by B rather than by K_2 as in equation 58, is seen to be

$$B = \frac{2\pi\sigma^3}{3}\left(1 - \frac{27}{8}\frac{D_e}{kT}\right). \qquad \ldots\ldots\ldots 80$$

When the same treatment is applied to the mixture, we obtain, using the same approximations, the isotherm

$$\frac{PV}{(N_1+N_2)kT} = 1 + \frac{2\pi(N_1+N_2)}{3V}\left[x_1^2\sigma_{11}^3\left(1 - \frac{27}{8}\frac{D_{11}}{kT}\right)\right.$$
$$\left. + x_2^2\sigma_{22}^3\left(1 - \frac{27}{8}\frac{D_{22}}{kT}\right) + 2x_1x_2\sigma_{12}^3\left(1 - \frac{27}{8}\frac{D_{12}}{kT}\right)\right], \qquad \ldots\ldots\ldots 81$$

where x denotes the molar fraction. The second virial coefficient in this case is the coefficient of $(N_1+N_2)/V$, and may therefore be written as follows:

$$B = x_1^2 B_{11} + x_2^2 B_{22} + 2x_1 x_2 B_{12}. \qquad \ldots\ldots\ldots 82$$

From experimental values of the virial coefficients of mixed gases at various temperatures, therefore, it is possible to evaluate the constants σ_{12} and D_{12} governing the interaction energy of a pair of unlike molecules. It is sometimes found that σ_{12} is nearly the arithmetic mean of σ_{11} and σ_{22}, as Berthelot had anticipated, and that D_{12} is roughly the geometric mean of D_{11} and D_{22}. When there is no experimental evidence, these simple relationships are often assumed.

IV

THE METALLIC STATE

MOST elementary metals crystallise in face-centred or body-centred cubic lattices. Their heats of sublimation range from about 20 to 200 kilocalories per gram-atom, and are higher by several orders of magnitude than those of the crystalline forms of the elements of group O in the periodic table. Their interatomic frequencies also are higher, but of the same order of magnitude. At ordinary temperatures, the heat capacities of most metallic elements lie close to $3R$ calories per gram-atom-degree. These facts can be adequately interpreted in terms of intermolecular forces, the relatively high heats of sublimation and interatomic vibration frequencies being attributed to the stronger forces of attraction in the metals. Many of the properties of mercury, for example, can, as we have seen, be accounted for by the interatomic energy equation $\phi = Aa^{-9} - Ba^{-6}$. By and large, however, Mie's equation is not directly applicable to metals.

Apart from their high densities and great hardness, the chief physical properties of metals that distinguish them from monatomic non-metals are their thermal and electrical conductivities. The magnitude of the latter suggests that roughly one electron per atom in a crystalline metal is able to move freely throughout the whole volume of the metal, just as if it were an atom in an ideal gas. A metal crystal can thus be regarded as a framework of cations in a cement of mobile electrons. Difficulties, however, arise from the adoption of such a model, particularly when attempting to explain why the heat capacity is very nearly $3R$ rather than $(9/2)R$, as would be the case if the electrons moved like gas atoms while the cations vibrated about their mean positions as three-dimensional oscillators.

The Fermi-Dirac statistics

The above argument is based on classical mechanics, and, though not very misleading as far as the nuclear vibrations are concerned, is otherwise fallacious. Fermi and Dirac have independently shown that electrons in metals are in regions where quantal laws prevail. Unlike atoms in a gas, where each can claim a phase-space cell for itself, the electrons in a metal have more than one cell apiece. This radically alters the statistics, and leads to the following approximate expression, due to Sommerfeld, for the translational partition function of the electron

$$f = e^{-\frac{3}{5}\frac{\varepsilon_o}{kT}} . e^{\frac{\pi^2}{4}\frac{kT}{\varepsilon_o}}, \qquad ....83$$

where the kinetic energy ε_o is given in terms of the mass, m_e, of the electron, and the concentration, n, of the electrons in the metal:

$$\varepsilon_o = \frac{h^2}{8m_e}\left(\frac{3}{\pi}n\right)^{2/3} . \qquad ....84$$

But for the factor $(3/\pi)^{\frac{2}{3}}$, this expression for the Fermi energy can be readily obtained by means of de Broglie's law ($m_e v = h/\lambda$) with the assumption that the associated wave-length λ is $2l$, where l^3 is the average volume of the metal occupied by one electron. The order of magnitude of ε_o is 100 kilocalories per gram-atom; its exact value depends on how many electrons in the metal are free, and this is difficult to determine precisely. It follows from this approximate partition function that the contribution of the electrons to the molar heat capacity is small, and equal to their contribution to the entropy:

$$C_e = R(\pi^2 kT/\varepsilon_o) = S_e. \qquad ....85$$

Moser's experimental value of the heat capacity of silver at 1000° K is 3·04R. The heat capacity, C_e, due to the electrons is thus 0·04R, and is consistent with the presence in the metal of 3 free electrons per atom of silver. It is in this way that the quantum theory has reconciled the thermal and electrical properties of metals.

The equivalent electrical conductivity of metals, according to this theory, is given approximately by the equation

$$\Lambda = \frac{8N_o e^2}{h}\left(\frac{\pi}{3n}\right)^{2/3} . \qquad ....86$$

Its value is greater by about 10^4 than the corresponding equivalent conductivity of electrolytes.

The kinetic treatment of the rate of emission of electrons from hot metals gives the following expression for the current density at temperature T, in terms of the mass, m_e and the charge, e, of the electron

$$i = \frac{4\pi m_e e(kT)^2}{h^3} . e^{-E/kT}, \qquad ....87$$

where E, the thermionic work term, is identical with $h\nu_o$ obtained from the threshold frequency ν_o of light which can induce the photoelectric emission of electrons at ordinary temperatures. The thermionic law was deduced by Richardson, using classical statistics to treat the electrons outside the metal. It can also be derived by applying the Fermi-Dirac statistics to electrons inside it.

While the new statistics have led to the present electron theory of metals and the elucidation of many of their properties which could not be understood in terms of classical statistics, there still remain many perplexing properties of metals and alloys which cannot be explained by the old or the new theory without introducing a new idea, namely, that of partial order (or partial disorder) in systems at equilibrium. There are several distinct and apparently unconnected properties of metals and alloys which have received their first logical interpretation in terms of the theory of order and disorder. Three of these are briefly discussed below.

Certain abnormal properties of metals and alloys

Alloys of copper and gold of all compositions can be made in the solid and liquid phases near their melting points; their physico-chemical properties vary smoothly and continuously as the composition is changed. At room temperatures, however, the isotherm of electrical resistance as a function of the composition passes through very sharp minima when the atomic ratios of gold to copper are 1 : 3 and 1 : 1. Moreover, the electrical resistance, r, of the 1 : 1 alloy, which at room temperatures is about twice as great as would be expected on an additivity basis, increases rapidly as the temperature, T, is raised until a temperature of 725° K is reached, after which dr/dT falls abruptly to a value which is the normal one for the pure metals (Fig. 11). The heat capacity, C_P, of a β-brass containing nearly the same number of atoms of copper as of zinc, agrees fairly closely at temperatures below 400° K with the mean of the heat capacities of the pure elements. Above this temperature, C_P rises to a sharp peak of $8R$ at 737° K, thereafter falling abruptly to about $4R$.

The structural analysis of freshly prepared copper-gold alloys by the method of X-ray reflexion shows that the lattice is a face-centred cubic one, like that of pure gold and copper, and that the sites are randomly occupied by atoms of both kinds. After annealing, however, it is found that the gold atoms occupy the points of a simple cubic

D

lattice, though the general structure of the alloy remains unchanged. These observations of Johannsen and Lindé (1925) confirmed a hypothesis due to Tammann (1919) according to which the annealing of binary alloys may cause atoms otherwise randomly occupying lattice sites to segregate into regular positions

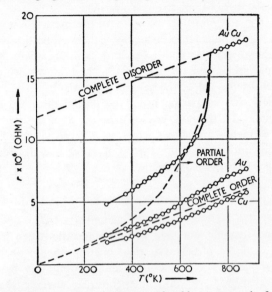

FIG. 11.   The specific electrical resistance of gold, copper and of a gold-copper alloy at various temperatures.   The points and continuous lines represent the experimental data of Kurnakow and Ageew.   The dotted lines are the theoretical values of Bragg and Williams and of Borelius.

Reprinted with permission from Moelwyn-Hughes, *Physical Chemistry* (1957), Pergamon Press Limited.

These diversified phenomena, and others, such as the appearance of the Curie point in the heat capacity-temperature curve of the ferromagnetic elements, have found a common explanation in terms of the theory of order and disorder (Weiss, 1919; Heisenberg, 1928; Gorsky, 1928; Bragg and Williams, 1934; Borelius, 1934; Bethé, 1935; Kirkwood, 1938).   The theory has latterly been applied to such difficult problems as melting, and the structure of liquids.

The theory of order and disorder in equimolar binary systems

Let us consider a crystal made up of a number, $N/2$, of atoms of type A, and an equal number of atoms of type B in a lattice having a number, $N/2$, of sites of type α and an equal number of sites of type β. The total number of sites in the crystal is thus N; and each site is occupied. If all the atoms of type A were on α sites, and all the atoms of type B were on β sites, we would have a completely ordered crystal, like that of common salt. Exchanges of sites are, however, possible, and if atoms of type A were to vacate their normal sites, atoms of type B would have to be accommodating by leaving their type of sites. The indiscriminate occupation of sites would destroy the orderliness of the crystal, and lead to a random distribution of atoms. The problem confronting us is the determination of the properties of the crystal when it is neither completely ordered nor completely disordered. To solve it, we first introduce a dimensionless term s, to denote the degree of order; s is unity when the system is completely ordered, and zero when the system is completely disordered. The standard procedure of statistical mechanics then leads to the solution

$$s = \tanh (ws/2kT) \qquad \ldots\ldots\ldots 88$$

where w is defined as follows in terms of the co-ordination number, c, and the interaction energies of neighbouring atomic pairs $A - A$, $B - B$ and $A - B$:

$$w = \frac{c}{2}(\phi_{AA} + \phi_{BB} - 2\phi_{AB}). \qquad \ldots\ldots\ldots 89$$

According to this solution, the degree of order is unity at the absolute zero of temperature; it decreases as the temperature is raised, until, when $T = w/2k$, it becomes zero. It is important to note that at temperatures higher than $w/2k$, s remains zero. Disorder can never be more than complete. As a consequence of the disorder, the free energy of the system is increased by an amount given by the equation

$$A = (\tfrac{1}{2})NkT[(1+s)\ln(1+s)+(1-s)\ln(1-s)-2\ln 2]+\tfrac{1}{4}Nw(1-s^2).$$
$$\ldots\ldots\ldots 90$$

It is seen at a glance that this expression gives the free energy possessed by the system in excess of the free energy of the completely ordered system. Fig. 12 shows how A varies with respect to s at three different temperatures.

The anomalous temperature variation of the electrical resistance of the copper-gold alloy has been independently explained in terms of equation 88 by Borelius (1934) and by Bragg and Williams (1934), who write for the specific resistance $r = sr_1 + (1-s)r_o$, where r_1 and

r_o denote, respectively, the specific resistance of the completely ordered and the completely disordered systems.

By standard thermodynamical argument, it follows that the contribution of the order-disorder effect to the heat capacity at constant volume is

$$C_v = R \cdot \frac{s^2(1-s^2)}{(2kT/w)^2[1-(2kT/w)(1-s^2)]}. \qquad \ldots\ldots\ldots 91$$

This relationship is found to be of the form required to account for the anomalous heat capacity of β-brass.

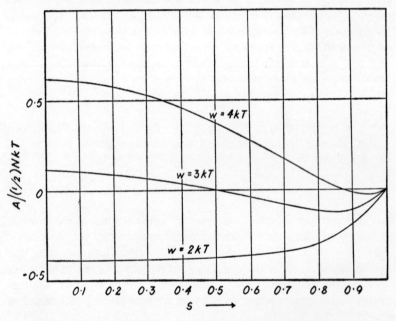

FIG. 12. Free energy as a function of the degree of order.

Ferromagnetic substances are characterised by the ease with which they become strongly magnetised even in weak external magnetic fields. Weiss (1921) and Heisenberg (1928) have explained the phenomenon along the lines of the order-disorder theory. In this problem, however, the randomness arises not from the possible occupancy of different sites but from the orientations of the atomic magnets. The terms ϕ_{AA}, ϕ_{BB} and ϕ_{AB} of equation 89 now refer to the interaction energies of a pair of neighbouring magnets, each of which lies in the direction of the field, a pair each of which lies in the direction opposed to the field, and a pair of which one lies with and the other against the direction of the field. The intensity of magnetisation, relative to its maximum value, is then found to be given by s of equation 88. The same theory explains why the heat capacity of the ferromagnetic elements exceeds that of the others, rises with temperature to a sharp maximum at the Curie point, and thereafter

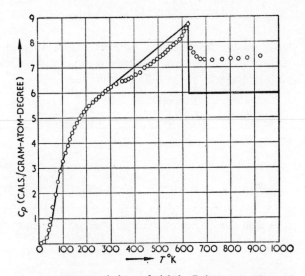

FIG. 13. The atomic heat of nickel. Points: experimental values of C_p. Lines: theoretical values of C_v.

Reprinted with permission from Moelwyn Hughes, *Physical Chemistry* (1957), Pergamon Press Limited.

abruptly falls. This is illustrated in Fig. 13 which shows the heat capacity of nickel at constant pressure, as measured by Busey and Giauque (1952) from 13° to 300° K and by Moser (1936) at higher temperatures. The continuous line is the theoretical equation for the heat capacity at constant volume obtained from equations 36 and 91:

$$C_v = 3R \left(\frac{hv_o}{2kT} \operatorname{cosech} \frac{hv_o}{2kT} \right)^2 + R \left\{ \frac{s^2(1-s^2)}{(T/T_c)^2[1-(T_c/T)(1-s^2)]} \right\} \quad \dots \dots 92$$

The first term is the contribution to the heat capacity due to the harmonic oscillations of the nickel atoms, and the second term, in which T_c stands for $w/2k$, is the contribution arising from the fact that the alignment of the magnets is only partly ordered.

V

THE LIQUID STATE

LIQUIDS constitute the intermediate state of matter through which solids normally pass into vapours. In most respects and requirements they are also intermediate, as the following summary shows:

State	Intermolecular forces	Ratio of mean free path to molecular diameter	Molecular arrangement	Statistics
Gas	weak	$\gg 1$	chaotic	classical
Solid	strong	$\ll 1$	orderly	quantal
Liquid	medium	~ 1	partially ordered	both

Except for the attention given it in recent years by numerous theorists, it is also the neglected state of matter, for relatively little new experimental work has been done upon it.

The analysis of liquids by means of the diffraction of X-rays

The Fourier analysis of the intensity of X-rays scattered from the surface of a liquid allows, in principle, a means of exploring the arrangement of the molecules in it (Prins, 1929; Mencke, 1932). There are, however, difficulties in interpreting the experimental results relating even to monatomic liquids.

If the molecular concentration, N/V, were uniform, the number, dN, of molecules in a spherical shell of thickness da at a distance a from some representative molecule would be $4\pi(N/V)a^2da$. It is known, however, from the structure of solids that N/V is far from uniform at small intermolecular separations. This fact can be allowed for by introducing a dimensionless factor, g, which is a function of a. Then $dN = 4\pi(N/V)a^2g(a)da$, and the average potential energy per molecule is

$$u = 2\pi(N/V) \int_{o}^{\infty} \phi(a)g(a)a^2da. \qquad \ldots\ldots\ldots 93$$

The form of the function g obtained by Hildebrand (1939) for 4 liquid metals is shown in Fig. 14. It is zero when a is zero, unity when a is large, and shows two maxima, the higher of which occurs at a distance slightly greater than the near-neighbour distance in the corresponding solid. The scattering data of Hildebrand, Wakeham and Boyd (1939) lead them to ascribe the 9-6 potential equation of Mie to liquid mercury, a result which, as we have noted, has been independently confirmed in other ways (Moelwyn-Hughes, 1951; Epstein and Powers, 1953).

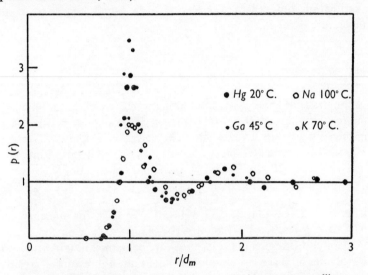

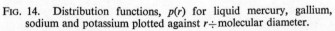

FIG. 14. Distribution functions, $p(r)$ for liquid mercury, gallium, sodium and potassium plotted against $r \div$ molecular diameter.

The same technique has been used to estimate the co-ordination number in liquids (Gringrich, 1943). Thus, for example, the average number of nearest neighbours in liquid nitrogen, oxygen and chlorine is 1, confirming that these elements are diatomic in the liquid state. For liquid lithium near its melting point, c is 9·8, denoting a departure from the body-centred cubic structure ($c = 8$) of the crystal, but for liquid potassium, c is 8, as it is in the crystal. c for grey tin is 4, in agreement with a diamond lattice; but for molten tin it is 10 near the melting point (505° K) and 8·9 at 663° K. Gringrich concludes that a definite change in the lattice pattern occurs on melting. With liquid argon near its melting point he finds $c = 10·6 \pm 0·4$. Thus the average number of near neighbours in this liquid is at least one less than in the crystal. Similar results are found with zinc and cadmium. Campbell and Hildebrand (1943) find c to be between 9 and 10 for liquid xenon, and to vary irregularly with respect to temperature.

As far as may be judged from the results on the relatively few liquids examined, a change in molecular arrangement may take place when a crystal melts. More usually, however, the arrangement of molecules in the liquid at the melting point seems vaguely to resemble that in the crystal, though with a lower co-ordination number. There is some scant experimental evidence to suggest that the average co-ordination number of a molecule in a liquid decreases as the temperature is raised.

The compressibility of liquids

Liquids as a class are more compressible than solids and much less compressible than gases. Excepting water, which has a minimum compressibility at about 45° C. (Amagat, 1893), liquids become more compressible as they are heated. The variation of the coefficient of the isothermal compressibility, β, with respect to temperature is in some instances well represented by the empirical equation

$$\beta = \beta_o e^{bT}, \qquad \qquad \ldots\ldots\ldots 94$$

where b is a constant (e.g. $1 \cdot 371 \times 10^{-3}$ deg.$^{-1}$ for mercury and $7 \cdot 97 \times 10^{-3}$ for normal pentane). The standard data on the subject, due mainly to Bridgman (1931; 1946) are contained in tables showing the volume of a given sample of liquid at a pressure P relative to its volume at unit pressure (1 kilogram per cm.^{2}). The first curve in Fig. 15, showing Bridgman's data for carbon disulphide at 20° C., is typical of most liquids, from the highly compressible normal pentane to the least compressible of liquids which is mercury. From this curve, the isothermal compressibility $\beta = -(1/V)(dV/dP)_T$ is readily evaluated. The second curve in Fig. 1 shows how β changes with respect to pressure. On its general form, Bridgman comments as follows:

" By far the most rapid decrease in compressibility occurs at low pressures; on an average, the compressibility has decreased to about one-half its initial value in the first 1000 kilograms. The natural explanation of this is that at low pressures the molecules fit loosely together with considerable free space between, and the major part of the compressibility at low pressures arises

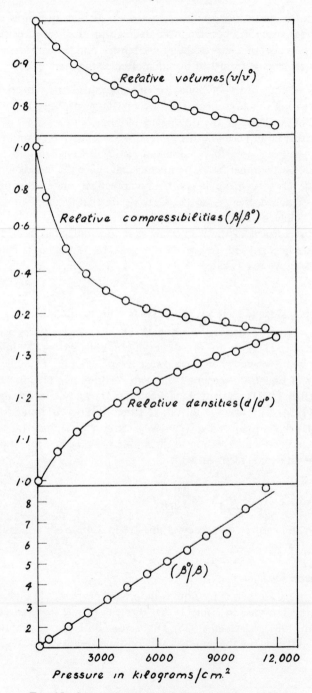

FIG. 15. Some properties of compressed CS_2 at 20° C.

from the occupancy of this free space; at high pressures, when the free space has become more or less squeezed out of existence, this easy sort of compressibility disappears, and the compressibility that remains is furnished by the molecules themselves ".

In terms of the theory of holes, or of unoccupied sites, it could be said, following this argument, that the first large decrease in β is due to the filling of holes or the occupancy of empty sites.

Whether liquids become incompressible under extreme compression has not yet been decided. Tammann (1912) believed this to be so. Bridgman, on the other hand, points out that, since the liquids hitherto examined have been found to be compressible under the highest pressures reached, there is no reason to doubt that further contraction would take place if still higher pressures were available.

The reciprocal of the isothermal compressibility has been found to increase linearly with respect to the pressure, so that, at a constant temperature, we may write

$$d(1/\beta)/dP = c, \qquad \ldots\ldots\ldots 95$$

where c is a constant. It has been shown that, for liquids which obey Mie's potential, c derived from data at low temperatures can be identified with $(1/3)(n+m+6)$ (Moelwyn-Hughes, 1951). The linearity is illustrated specifically in the lowest graph of Fig. 15, and more generally in Fig. 16. Accepting the data of Bridgman (1935), Gibson and Loeffler (1941), Newitt and Weale (1951) and Bett, Weale and Newitt (1954), the average deviation from linearity is found not to exceed 4 per cent. for water ($c = 6\cdot7$), carbon disulphide ($c = 7\cdot3$), mercury ($c = 8\cdot2$) and carbon tetrachloride ($c = 9\cdot35$). Equation 95, it may be shown, is identical with

$$\frac{d \ln \beta}{d \ln V} = c, \qquad \ldots\ldots\ldots 96$$

which for some purposes expresses this low in a more convenient form.

An isotherm for liquids

Empirical isotherms for liquids have been proposed, in differential or integrated forms, by Tait (1818), Biron (1912), Tammann (1912), Bridgman (1931), Macleod (1936), Hudleston (1937) and several others. Though differing in the number of constants employed, they bear,

on the whole, the marks of considerable similarity. A relatively simple
and more recent isotherm, with some theoretical basis, may be obtained
by integrating equation 95. According to it, the volume, V, of a
system at a pressure, P, becomes

$$V = V^o[1 + c\beta^o(P - P^o)]^{-\frac{1}{c}}, \qquad \ldots\ldots\ldots 97$$

where V^o is its volume and β^o its isothermal compressibility at some

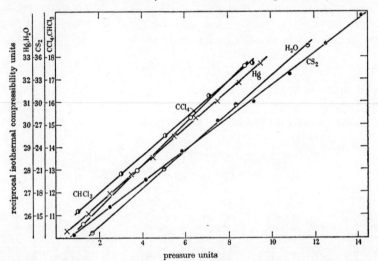

FIG. 16. Reciprocal isothermal compressibility as a function of pressure for
carbon tetrachloride and chloroform at 25° C. and carbon disulphide, mercury
and water at 40° C. Pressure units: 100 Kg./cm.² (CCl₄, CHCl₃); 150 Kg./cm.²
(H₂O); 300 Kg./cm.² (CS₂); 1000 Kg./cm² (Hg). Reciprocal compressibility
units: 1000 Kg./cm.² (CS₂, CCl₄, CHCl₃, H₂O); 10,000 Kg./cm.² (Hg).

reference pressure, P^o. The Gibbs free energy may then be expressed
in terms of the pressure or the volume:

$$G = G^o + \frac{V^o}{(c-1)\beta^o}\left\{[1 + c\beta^o(P - P^o)]^{\frac{c-1}{c}} - 1\right\} \qquad \ldots\ldots\ldots 98$$

$$= G^o + \frac{V^o}{(c-1)\beta^o}\left[\left(\frac{V^o}{V}\right)^{c-1} - 1\right]. \qquad \ldots\ldots\ldots 99$$

The theoretical derivation of these equations limits their validity to
values of V^o/V differing but slightly from unity.

The heat capacity of liquids at constant pressure

The molar heat capacity of a liquid at constant pressure and at the freezing point is generally slightly greater than that of the solid and considerably greater than that of the vapour at the same temperature. With many of the compounds investigated by Giauque and his collaborators, measurements on the heat capacities of crystals have been extended to the liquids. In certain instances, C_P for the liquid passes through a slight minimum at a temperature not far above the freezing point. The heat capacities of such liquids may be summarised empirically by the equation

$$C_P = K_0 + K_1 T + K_2 T^2. \qquad \ldots\ldots\ldots 100$$

The equation applies between the melting temperature, T_m, and the boiling temperature, T_b. Some values are given in Table 6. In terms of these constants, the Gibbs free energy of the liquid, relative to its

TABLE 6

$$C_P(\text{calories/mole-degree}) = K_0 + K_1 T + K_2 T^2$$

Liquid	T_m	T_b	K_0	$K_1 \times 10^2$	$K_2 \times 10^4$
Cl_2	172·12	239·05	14·850	+1·55	−0·500
CS_2	161·17	319·3	18·47	−0·495	+0·123
$COCl_2$	144·36	280·66	37·45	−12·75	+2·965
CH_3Cl	175·44	148·94	13·393	−5·568	+1·378
CH_3Br	179·44	276·66	25·511	−6·439	+1·463
$(CH_3)_3N$	156·08	276·03	32·197	−6·475	+2·250

value at the melting temperature, is given by the equation:

$$G = G_m - T K_0 \ln(T/T_m) + (K_0 - K_1 T)(T - T_m)$$
$$+ (\tfrac{1}{2})(K_1 - K_2 T)(T^2 - T_m^2) + (\tfrac{1}{3})(T^3 - T_m^3). \qquad \ldots\ldots\ldots 101$$

The entropy of liquids, and its variation with respect to temperature and pressure

By adding the entropy of fusion, L_m/T_m, to the entropy of the crystal at the melting point, the absolute entropy of the liquid at T_m is obtained. When the heat capacity varies with respect to temperature as in equation 100, the dependence of the entropy on T is found, by differentiating equation 101, to be

$$S = S_m + K_0 \ln(T/T_m) + K_1(T - T_m) + (\tfrac{1}{2})K(T^2 - T_m^2). \qquad \ldots\ldots\ldots 102$$

Before the entropy of a liquid at a given temperature, T, pressure, P, and volume V, can be related to its entropy S^o at the same temperature when in some reference state (pressure, P^o, and volume V^o), its isotherm must be known. If we accept that given by equation 97, we find

$$S = S^o - \frac{V^o b}{(c-1)\beta^o}\left\{\left(1 - \frac{1}{c}\right)\left(\frac{V^o}{V}\right)^{-1}\left[\left(\frac{V^o}{V}\right)^c - 1\right]\right.$$
$$\left. - \left(1 - \frac{\alpha_o}{b}\right)\left[\left(\frac{V^o}{V}\right)^{c-1} - 1\right]\right\}, \quad\ldots\ldots103$$

where α_o is the coefficient of cubical expansion at the pressure P^o.

The question has sometimes been raised as to whether high compression can reduce the entropy of a liquid to zero at ordinary temperatures. There appears to be no reason to doubt that tremendous compressions at ponderable temperatures can render molecules as immobile as when they are completely deprived of heat. Such computations as can be made, however, show that liquids under great compression at ordinary temperatures still retain considerable entropy. To determine the entropy of liquid carbon disulphide under high pressure at 298·16° K, we may use the following data:

$S^o = 36\cdot10$ cals./mole-degree (Brown and Manov, 1937).
$V^o = 60\cdot56$ c.c./mole. $c = 7\cdot3$.
$\beta^o = 9\cdot33 \times 10^{-5}$ atm.$^{-1}$ $b = 6\cdot73 \times 10^{-3}$ deg.$^{-1}$.
$\alpha_o = 1\cdot188 \times 10^{-3}$ deg.$^{-1}$.

The molar volume found by Bridgman at a pressure of 11,300 atmospheres is 45·26 c.c./mole. The decrease in entropy according to equation 103 is 7·15 cals./mole-degree, which is rather less than one-fifth of the total entropy at atmospheric pressure.

If the isotherm on which equation 103 is based were applicable at the high temperatures where b was measured, we would have

$$\frac{b}{\alpha^o} = c, \quad\ldots\ldots104$$

and the entropy change would simplify to

$$S = S^o - (\alpha^o/\beta^o)(V^o - V), \quad\ldots\ldots105$$

which implies that $(dP/dT)_V$ is independent of the volume. The isotherm, however, is known to be inapplicable at high temperatures, and the values of c obtained from equation 104 are always too low, e.g. 5·7 for CS_2 and 6·1 for CCl_4.

The heat capacity of liquids at constant volume

As the heat capacity at a constant volume V cannot be measured directly without using high pressures, it is usually obtained indirectly by means of the equation

$$C_V = C_P - \frac{(\alpha^o)^2 T V^o}{\beta^o} + \int_{V^o}^{V} \left(\frac{dC_V}{dV}\right)_{TV} dV. \quad\quad\ldots\ldots\ldots 106$$

Here C_P is the heat capacity at constant pressure, and the terms V^o, α^o and β^o denote the molar volume, the coefficient of isobaric expansion and the coefficient of isothermal compression at that constant pressure, which is generally one atmosphere. The last term is evaluated by substituting $T(d^2P/dT^2)_V$ for $(dC_V/dV)_T$. Experimental values obtained for carbon tetrachloride by Harrison and Moelwyn-Hughes (1957) are given in Table 7. The last column gives the heat capacity of the liquid at the melting volume, V_m. An increase in C_V with a rise in

TABLE 7

The heat capacities of liquid carbon tetrachloride
(calories/mole-degree)

T^oK	C_P	C_{V^o}	C_{V_m}
250·2	31·07	21·79	21·79
270	31·24	21·60	22·13
290	31·41	21·81	22·56
310	31·58	22·12	22·96
330	31·75	22·48	23·46
349·9	31·93	22·92	24·02

temperature is fairly typical of liquids, though not general. C_V for mercury at the melting volume decreases steadily from 6·028 at the melting temperature to 5·355 at the boiling point. Michels and Strijland (1952) find that C_V for liquid carbon dioxide at densities approaching the critical density increases up to the critical temperature, and thereafter falls sharply. $(dC_V/dV)_T$ is found to be negative for most liquids, including mercury and carbon tetrachloride, but positive for water (Bridgman, 1911; Gibson and Loeffler, 1941). The effect in either case is quantitatively given by the isotherm of equation 97.

Discussion of the heat capacities of liquids

Precise data on the heat capacities of liquids at constant volume can, in principle, throw light on the type of motion executed by a molecule in the liquid, as Bernal (1937), Eucken (1948) and Staveley,

Hart and Tupman (1953) have emphasised. When, for example, the values of C_V for various diatomic and monatomic liquids are plotted as a function of their reduced temperatures, T/T_c, the points fall on two curves which, despite their curious shapes, are separated by an approximately constant amount R, indicating that the diatomic molecules are rotating freely. To study more complicated molecules, the total heat capacity at constant volume may be resolved into four contributions arising from (1) the motion of the centre of gravity of the molecule, (2) internal vibrations, (3) rotation about the axes passing through the centre of gravity and (4) a change in the structure of the liquid. These contributions taken in order may be denoted by C with an appropriate subscript:

$$C_V = C_c + C_i + C_r + C_a. \qquad \ldots\ldots\ldots 107$$

Applied to carbon tetrachloride at the melting point, Harrison and Moelwyn-Hughes (1957) proceed as follows, giving the heat capacities in calories per mole-degree:

C_V (observed)	21·79
C_c (assumed equal to C_V for mercury) . . .	6·03
C_i (calculated from spectroscopic constants for the gas)	10·77
C_r (assuming free rotation)	2·98
Residue unaccounted for	2·01

From a similar analysis of the data for chloroform, there appears a residue of 3·50. If the rotation, instead of being free, were a fully torsional oscillation, a further amount of 2·98 could be subtracted, thus leaving a residue of 0·52 for $CHCl_3$, and more than accounting for the total heat capacity of CCl_4. Hindered rotations are intermediate in character, and probably play a part. Even so, it seems clear that if the total heat capacities of these liquids contain a component attributable to structural changes at constant volume, the contribution probably does not exceed R. With water, however, after allowing full torsional oscillations, there remains the considerable residuum of $3R$, leaving no doubt that much of the energy absorbed by this liquid when heated at constant volume is utilised in structural reorangisation.

Vaporization

Most of the accurate vapour pressure data available on liquids (Stull, 1947) can be expressed in terms of the empirical equation of

Kirchhoff (1858), Rankine (1866) and Dupré (1869),

$$\log_{10} p = a - b \log_{10} T - c/T. \qquad \dots\dots108$$

In regions where the vapour obeys the ideal gas laws, the molar heat of vaporization is then

$$L_T = L_s - bRT, \qquad \dots\dots109$$

where L_s is the heat of vaporization of the liquid subcooled to the absolute zero of temperature. The variation of the number b from one liquid to another has been interpreted in terms of a kinetic theory of vapour pressure (Moelwyn-Hughes and Rideal, 1937; Matthews, Sumner and Moelwyn-Hughes, 1950) according to which the escape of a molecule from the liquid to the vapour phase generally requires the distribution of its energy among a number s of classical oscillators. Then

$$b = s - (\tfrac{3}{2}). \qquad \dots\dots110$$

To the nearest whole number, s is found to be 3, 4, 5 and 6 for most monatomic, diatomic, triatomic and tetratomic liquids respectively. For straight-chained hydrocarbons containing n carbon atoms per molecule, s is approximately $2 + 0 \cdot 94n$. With the corresponding monohydric alcohols s is $4 + 1 \cdot 88n$. In both series there appear to be cumulative contributions to the heat of vaporization, L_s, from each of the methylene groups. In terms of the number, n_σ, of molecules on unit area of the liquid surface, their average vibration frequency, $\bar{v}$ and mass, μ, the approximate expression for the vapour pressure is

$$p = \frac{n_\sigma (2\pi\mu kT)^{\frac{1}{2}} \bar{v}}{(s-1)!} \left(\frac{\lambda_s}{kT}\right)^{s-1} \left[1 + (s-1)\left(\frac{kT}{\lambda_s}\right)\right] e^{-\lambda s/kT}. \qquad \dots\dots111$$

A second approximation leads to the logarithmic expression

$$\ln p = \text{constant} - (s-\tfrac{3}{2}) \ln T + (s+1)\left(\frac{kT}{\lambda_s}\right) - \frac{\lambda_s}{kT} \qquad \dots\dots112$$

which has the form used by Michels (1953) to reproduce the accurate vapour pressure data obtained by him on numerous liquids. The special cases where s is 3/2 and unity have been dealt with by Jellinek (1915) and Rodebush (1923) respectively. The case where s is 2 corresponds to monatomic liquids acting as systems of classical oscillators, and, applied to a face-centred cubic arrangement of particles subject to Mie's potential, yields the vapour pressure equation

$$p = \frac{2kT}{v_s}\left(\frac{mn\lambda_s}{6\pi kT}\right)^{\frac{3}{2}} e^{-\lambda s/kT} = \frac{2RT}{V_s}\left(\frac{mnL_s}{6\pi RT}\right)^{\frac{3}{2}} e^{-L_s/RT}. \qquad \dots\dots113$$

It follows that Trouton's ratio L_b/RT_b for a series of liquids increases linearly with respect to T_c/V_c (cf. Barclay and Butler, 1938). Hildebrand (1918) has argued that the entropy of vaporization for a set of liquids should be compared with one another not at their boiling points, T_b, but at temperatures, T_a, at which the vapours have all the same high molar volume, V_G. The resulting ratio

$$\frac{L_T}{RT_a} = \ln\left[2\left(\frac{mnL_s}{6\pi RT_a}\right)^{\frac{3}{2}}\right] - \tfrac{1}{2} + \ln\left(\frac{V_G}{V_s}\right) \qquad \ldots\ldots\ldots 114$$

is found to be more constant than Trouton's.

Fusion

When the crystalline and liquid phases of a pure substance are at equilibrium, the chemical potentials in the two phases are equal. There have been several attempts to arrive at the chemical potential, and thence the partition function, of a liquid by combining theoretical expressions for the solid with experimental data on the heat and entropy of fusion.

If in both phases the molecules act as harmonic oscillators, the molar energy and entropy of fusion would be $\Delta E_m = N_o(u_{\text{liq}} - u_{\text{cr}})$ and $\Delta S_m = 3R \ln (v_{\text{cr}}/v_{\text{liq}})$, where the u and v terms can be calculated by means of equations 25 and 26. Both magnitudes derived in this way fall far below the actual values. If, however, the oscillators in the liquid phase can freely interchange their sites, the entropy of fusion is given by the expression

$$\Delta S_m/R = 1 + 3\ln(v_{\text{cr}}/v_{\text{liq}}). \qquad \ldots\ldots\ldots 115$$

The major contribution to ΔS_m is thus R, which Hirschfelder, Stevenson and Eyring (1937) have termed the communal entropy. With reasonable estimates of $v_{\text{cr}}/v_{\text{liq}}$, $\Delta S_m/R$ for mercury becomes $1 \cdot 267$, in close agreement with the experimental value of $1 \cdot 185$.

A radical structural change, as, for example, from a face-centred to a body-centred arrangement, can also explain the magnitude of the heat of fusion, but X-ray evidence rules this explanation out, except in special cases.

Lennard-Jones and Devonshire (1937) have treated the liquid inert elements at their melting temperatures as systems of partial order s, while the crystalline states are considered to be completely ordered ($s = 1$). From equation 90, the molar gain in energy on melting is

E

given by the equation

$$\Delta E_m = (\tfrac{1}{2})N_o w(1-s^2) = \tfrac{1}{2}W(1-s^2). \qquad \ldots\ldots\ldots 116$$

If s for the liquid at the melting temperature were $\tfrac{1}{2}$, W would be $3RT_m$ (Fig. 12) and the entropy of fusion would be $(9/8)R$, which is in still closer agreement with experiment. As far as the fusion of crystalline mercury is concerned, the theory of order and disorder would thus appear to be sufficient, provided that s for the liquid is $\tfrac{1}{2}$. This degree of order, however, would endow the liquid with a heat capacity exceeding $3R$ by an amount $0\cdot 36R$, which is much too great (Moelwyn-Hughes, 1958). Further treatments of fusion have been given by Born (1954) and Temperley (1956).

Viscosity

Many of the recent theories of the viscosity of liquids (Frenkel, 1925; Andrade, 1934; Eyring, 1936) have, not unnaturally, concentrated on interpreting the two positive constants in an empirical equation

$$\eta = Ae^{B/RT} \qquad \ldots\ldots\ldots 117$$

which has been found crudely to reproduce the decrease in the viscosity of a liquid when it is heated at constant pressure. A critical analysis of this equation, however, shows that neither A nor B is strictly constant. B, for example, increases as the temperature is raised in the case of non-polar liquids. The kinetic theory of gases, treating molecules as incompressible spheres of diameter, σ, transferring momentum only in those collisions where the energy exceeds a value ε, provides the expression

$$\eta = \frac{1}{\pi\sigma^2}\left(\frac{kTm}{\pi}\right)^{\tfrac{1}{2}} e^{\varepsilon/kT} \qquad \ldots\ldots\ldots 118$$

which has the required form, and indicates a decrease in η when the fluid is heated at constant volume and at temperatures below $2\varepsilon/k$. To compare equations 117 and 118 directly, however, is illegitimate, and has proved to be misleading. The total effect of temperature on the viscosity of a liquid is, at least, a double effect. One is its effect on the frequency with which liquid molecules move or vibrate; the other and more important effect is that of altering the average intermolecular separation, a.

Andrade, regarding a molecule in a liquid as an oscillator with an average frequency, v, has suggested that the transfer of momentum occurs $2v$ times per second between molecules in neighbouring moving layers. For a face-centred cubic arrangement of molecules, his expression for A becomes $(2)^{\frac{1}{2}}(mv/a)$, where m is the mass and a the intermolecular distance. Different numerical terms appear in liquids with other arrangements. Moelwyn-Hughes (1932) has also argued that the viscosity is directly proportional to the vibration frequency, and has derived a very similar relationship between them. Andrade has successfully correlated the viscosity of certain metals and diatomic liquids with vibration frequencies calculated from their compressibilities and heat capacities. An interesting feature of Eyring's treatment is a virtual identification of λ in the classical equation for gases, $\eta = (\frac{1}{3})mn\lambda c$, with de Broglie's wave length $\lambda = h/mc$, so that A becomes $(\frac{1}{3})nh$. This treatment offers an explanation of an approximate constancy found by Dunstan (1914) in the product of the viscosity and molar volume V_m for many series of unassociated liquids. The data for liquid mercury may be summarised in the equation

$$\eta V_m = 8\cdot52 \times 10^{-2} e^{581/RT}. \qquad \ldots\ldots\ldots 119$$

The anticipated value of the pre-exponential term is $(\frac{1}{3})N_o h = 2 \times 10^{-3}$. The discrepancy with other liquids is larger.

Batschinski (1913) has argued that the viscosity of a liquid is a function of its volume only, but experiments by Bridgman may be cited to show that this is not true.

If the variation of the viscosity of liquids when they are heated at constant volume is provisionally assumed to be given by an equation of the form

$$\eta = C(V)e^{B_V/RT} \qquad \ldots\ldots\ldots 120$$

the energy B_V may be evaluated. It is found to be smaller than B_P, and in fact, for many liquids, to be approximately $(\frac{1}{3})RT$, so that the simpler law

$$\eta = C(V)T^{\frac{1}{3}} \qquad \ldots\ldots\ldots 121$$

may well hold. More new facts on the combined effects of temperature and pressure on viscosity, such as those found by Jobling and Lawrence (1951), are needed before theory can be further developed.

Theories of the liquid state

Much is demanded of a satisfactory theory of any liquid, even when it is monatomic. It must explain, for example, the decrease in volume, heat and entropy which usually attend its solidification. It must account for a heat capacity which, at the triple point, is nearly that of a classical harmonic oscillator, though possibly still under quantal control, and its steady decrease as the temperature is raised at constant volume, to the critical point. It must explain why the heat capacity, at constant temperature and volume, varies with the volume in such a way that a maximum is reached at the critical volume. The coefficients of isobaric expansion and of isothermal compression must also be accounted for as functions of the volume (or pressure) and temperature. It is, perhaps, not surprising that no single theory yet advanced has proved capable of coping with the whole situation. Monographs on the subject (e.g. Frenkel, 1946; Rowlinson, 1959) may be consulted for fuller accounts of some of the attempts that have been made. We shall here briefly review some distinctive approaches to the problem.

Free space theories have been abundantly advanced, and would have achieved greater success had free space been regarded as Boltzmann defined it rather than as what is left over when the volume of a number of incompressible spheres is subtracted from the total volume of the system they form. It is a simple matter to derive expressions for the true free space in liquids in terms of empirical constants governing their vapour pressures, but they represent less a theory of liquids than a correlation of some of their observable properties.

Free space finely divided provides holes; and the hole theory of liquids has been largely developed, especially for holes of equal size, and, for still greater simplicity, for holes of molecular size (Altar, 1936; Fürth, 1936; Eyring, 1937). The decrease in orthobaric density of liquids as the temperature is raised may then be regarded as an increase in the concentration of holes, and viscosity can be treated as the movement of holes in a direction counter to that of the molecules.

The harmonic oscillator theory has been amended in various ways in attempts to account for the properties of liquids. An arbitrary limit may be placed on the amplitude, or anharmonicity terms added to the elastic energy.

A general approach to the problem is provided by the virial theorem, but, even with the simplest law of force that can command attention, computational difficulties arise in its application.

Partition functions have been derived for plausible molecular models, such as that of a molecule which at high concentrations acts like an oscillator and at low concentrations like a gas molecule (Lennard-Jones and Devonshire, 1937). Even when developed with exactitude, they fail, however, in some respects. For example, force laws based on the most condensed state of the liquid fail to reproduce the critical conditions, and a degree of order necessary to account for the expansion of the crystal on melting is incapable of accounting for the heat capacity.

From the theoretical standpoint, the liquid state can no longer be regarded as neglected, but it still remains the least understood of the states of matter.

VI

THE DISSOLVED STATE

PHYSICAL chemistry originated with the study of solutions, and these continue to be its principal concern. For the present purpose, a solution is defined as a condensed, fluid and homogeneous system containing not less than two components. Solid solutions and mixtures of gases are thus excluded. In binary systems the component present in the smaller amount is called the solute: that in the large amount the solvent. But the distinction is arbitrary.

A clue concerning the nature of dissolved molecules is provided by the thermal effects attending the dissolution of the halogens in water under ordinary conditions. The dissolution of iodine is endothermic: that of bromine athermic, and that of chlorine exothermic. Moreover, the heat absorbed when crystalline iodine dissolves in water is nearly the same as its heat of fusion, and the heat evolved when gaseous chlorine dissolves in the same solvent is nearly the same as its heat of condensation into a liquid. The status of dissolved molecules thus appears to be that of a liquid.

Solutions which conduct electricity have properties differing so widely from those of their components that they are treated separately under the title of electrolytes.

A rough and ready rule indicating when dissolution can occur is that like dissolves like. Neighbouring members in any series of homologous hydrocarbons, for example, are mutually soluble in all proportions. The mutual solubilities of carbon tetrachloride and water, on the other hand, are extremely low, though measurable. Similarity in the internal pressures,—du/dv, and in the energy densities u/v has been detected by Hildebrand (1921) as quantitative guides to the mutual solubility of liquids—a conclusion to which a statistical interpretation has been given in terms of intermolecular forces.

Ideal solutions

When the partial pressure p_1 exerted by one component in the vapour which is at equilibrium with the solution is proportional to its molar fraction x_1 in the liquid over its whole range of composition (Raoult's law, 1888) the solution is said to be ideal. The proportionality factor is clearly p_1^o, the vapour pressure of the pure liquid at the temperature of the solution. The partial pressures are consequently

$$p_1 = p_1^o x_1 \quad \text{and} \quad p_2 = p_2^o x_2 \qquad \ldots\ldots\ldots 122$$

and the total pressure is

$$P = p_1 + p_2 = x_1 p_1^o + x_2 p_2^o. \qquad \ldots\ldots\ldots 123$$

This law is seldom obeyed accurately, except with isomers, but for wide ranges of liquids the actual behaviour approximates fairly closely to the linear relationships implied. Fig. 17 shows the slight but significant deviations found in the methyl iodide-methylene dichloride system at 25° C. It is seen that the law, though simple and almost empirical, achieves the main object of the theory of solution, which is to determine its properties from those of its components. Raoult's law implies that the chemical potential of a molecule in an ideal binary solution is given by the equation

$$\mu_1 = \mu_1^o + kT \ln x_1 = \mu_1^o + kT \ln \left(\frac{N_1}{N_1 + N_2} \right), \qquad \ldots\ldots\ldots 124$$

when the N's are the numbers of molecules in the solution, and μ_1^o is the chemical potential of one molecule of the first kind in its pure liquid state. Some of its consequences are that the osmotic pressure of an ideal solution is given in terms of the molecular volume v_1 of the solvent, which is assumed to be incompressible, by the equation

$$\Pi = \frac{kT}{v_1} \ln \left(\frac{N_1 + N_2}{N_1} \right), \qquad \ldots\ldots\ldots 125$$

and that the lowering in the freezing point T_1^o of the solvent is given approximately by the equation

$$T_1^o - T_1 = \frac{RT_1^o T_1}{L_T} \ln \left(\frac{N_1 + N_2}{N_1} \right), \qquad \ldots\ldots\ldots 126$$

where L_T is its molar heat of fusion at the freezing point T_1 of the solution. In dilute solutions, equation 125 approximates to $\Pi = (kT/v_1)(N_2/N_1)$, and, since $N_1 v_1$ is now effectively the volume V of the solution, we arrive at the well-known law of van't Hoff (1887)

$$\Pi = kT n_2, \qquad \ldots\ldots\ldots 127$$

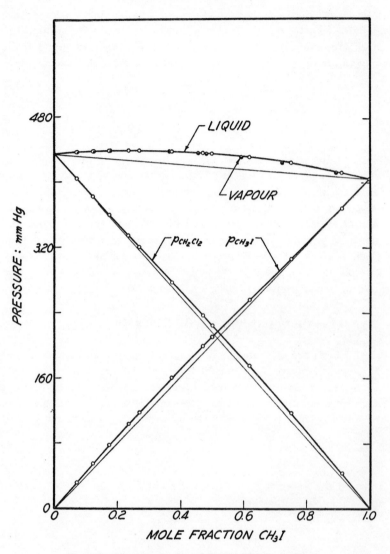

FIG. 17. Vapour pressure of CH_3I—CH_2Cl_2 at 25° C.

where n_2 is the concentration of solute in molecules per c.c. Similarly, the depression in the freezing point approximates to $(RT_1^o T_1/L_T)(N_2/N_1)$. If w grams of solute (of molar weight M_2) are dissolved in 100 grams of solvent (of molar weight M_1), then $N_2/N_1 = (w/M_2)/(100/M_1)$, so that

$$T_1^o - T_1 = \left(\frac{RT_1^oT_1}{100\ l_T}\right)\frac{w}{M_2}. \qquad \text{.........128}$$

l_T denotes the heat of fusion per gram of solvent. This equation has long been used in the determination of molar weights (Beckmann, 1897), particularly those of compounds like carbohydrates and proteins.

Deviations from ideality

(i) *Solvation*

Raoult's law in its original form was expressed as follows:

$$\frac{p_1^o - p_1}{p_1^o} = \frac{N_2}{N_1 + N_2}, \qquad \text{.........122a}$$

from which we see that the relative lowering in the partial pressure of one component is equal to the molar fraction of the other component. Poynting (1896) posed the question: how can a solute like sucrose, which itself is relatively involatile, bring about a marked lowering in the partial pressure of water ? One answer is that sucrose molecules combine with water molecules in such a way as to diminish or even completely to remove their ability to contribute to the total pressure of the solution. If each molecule of solute were to combine with c molecules of solvent to form an involatile complex, the number of solvent molecules free to contribute to the pressure would be reduced from N_1 to $N_1 - cN_2$. Equation 125 must then be amended to

$$\Pi = \frac{kT}{v_1}\ln\left[1 + \frac{N_2}{N_1 - cN_2}\right] \qquad \text{.........129}$$

which, as Callendar (1908) and Findlay (1914) found, is in good agreement with the facts if c is taken as 5. The agreement with the standard data of Berkeley and Hartley (1906) is even better with $c = 6$ (Fig. 18). The solvate theory of Poynting and Callendar has thus much support *a posteriori*. Though long neglected, it is coming into its own again, particularly in the treatment of electrolytes. Salts like lithium fluoride in water almost certainly incapacitate several molecules of water per mole of salt. This supposition readily explains, for example, why the partial molar volume and heat capacity of this salt in water are negative.

Solvates can often be obtained in crystalline form from solution. Faraday isolated a crystalline hydrate of chlorine of composition

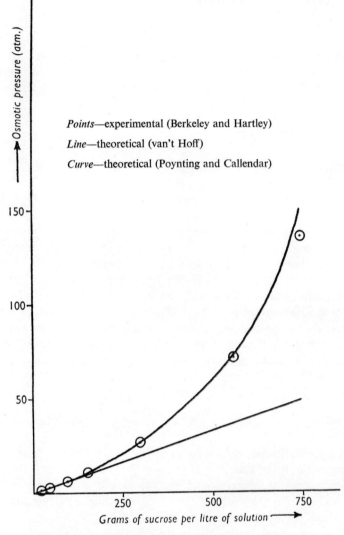

Points—experimental (Berkeley and Hartley)

Line—theoretical (van't Hoff)

Curve—theoretical (Poynting and Callendar)

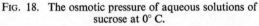

Fig. 18. The osmotic pressure of aqueous solutions of sucrose at 0° C.

Cl_2, $8H_2O$. A more exact stoichiometric formula $6Cl_2$, $46H_2O$ has since been established by X-ray crystallography (Pauling and Marsh, 1952). Lowry and Traill (1932) suspected solvation of beryllium benzoyl camphor (*A*) in chloroform solution, and isolated a crystalline compound of composition A, $2CHCl_3$. It is thus possible that solvates, even in rich variety, often exist in solution although their crystalline forms have yet to be isolated.

(ii) *Dimerisation*

Polar molecules in the gaseous phase and in solvents of low dielectric constants (D) are apt to form dimers. A thoroughly investigated group of such dimers are those formed from carboxylic acids. The bonds holding the pair together were termed hydrogen bonds by Latimer and Rodebush (1920), who postulated the linear structure

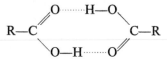

which has since been confirmed by the method of electron diffraction (Pauling and Brockway, 1934). For a time the binding energy was attributed to a wave-mechanical effect known as resonance, but since 1938, opinion has slowly changed in favour of the present view, which is that the attractive energy is due to the electrostatic interaction of the four permanent dipoles in the pair. The precise and extensive information now available on the stability of these dimers in the gaseous phase and in solution is consistent with the following expression for the potential energy:

$$u = \left(\frac{3}{n} - 1\right) 4\mu_A \mu_B \cos \theta_A \cos \theta_B / Da^3. \qquad \ldots\ldots\ldots 130$$

n is the integer appearing in equation 1, and is generally taken as 9. μ_A and μ_B are the bond moments of the carboxyl and hydroxyl radicals; a is the distance apart of their centres, and θ_A and θ_B the angles at which the dipoles are inclined to the line of centres. Many of the properties of solutions of polar molecules have been explained in terms of this equation.

(iii) *Intermolecular complex formation*

Dolezalek and Schultze (1910) have been able to explain many of the properties of binary liquid mixtures by assuming that Raoult's law is obeyed not only by the single molecules A and B but by intermolecular complexes AB and dimers A_2 or B_2, which may be formed from them. Consistent with the assumption of the universal validity of Raoult's law, the law of mass action becomes applicable, in terms of molar fractions, to equilibria such as $A + B \rightleftharpoons AB$ in solution. When no dimers are formed, for example, the number of intermolecular complexes in solution is given by the equation

$$N_c = \frac{N_1(p_2/p_2^o) - N_2(p_1/p_1^o)}{(p_2/p_2^o) - (p_1/p_1^o)}. \qquad \dots\dots131$$

Along these lines, apparent deviations from Raoult's law can be attributed, when positive, to dimerisation of one component, and when negative, to the formation of an intermolecular complex. Much evidence could be cited in support of these arguments. The carboxylic acids, for example, are unquestionably dimerised to varying degrees in a variety of solvents. Eutectic mixtures are often of stoichiometric proportions. Negative deviations from Raoult's law are chiefly found in liquid mixtures formed from highly polar molecules, such as chloroform and acetone. In short, the soundness of Dolezalek's argument cannot be challenged. What remains is to find in what systems and under what conditions the specific or chemical interaction of molecules is more probable than the general or physical interaction.

Regular solutions

An expression for the Helmholtz free energy, A, of a homogeneous system containing N_1 molecules of one kind and N_2 molecules of another kind can be readily derived provided the molecules are isomegethic (i.e. of equal size) and mix freely. In terms of the molecular partition functions, f_1 and f_2, and the molecular potential energies, u_1^o and u_2^o, of the pure components, the free energy of the system at a temperature, T, is found to be:

$$A = N_1\left[-kT\ln f_1 + u_1^o + kT\ln\left(\frac{N_1}{N_1+N_2}\right)\right]$$

$$+ N_2\left[-kT\ln f_2 + u_2^o + kT\ln\left(\frac{N_2}{N_1+N_2}\right)\right]$$

$$+ \frac{N_1N_2}{N_1+N_2}\Delta u^o. \qquad \dots\dots132$$

The interchange energy, Δu^o is related as follows to the co-ordination number, c, and the interaction energies of the three relevant molecular pairs:

$$\Delta u^o = c \left(\phi_{1,2} - \tfrac{1}{2}\,\phi_{1,1} - \tfrac{1}{2}\phi_{2,2} \right). \qquad \dots\dots133$$

The thermodynamic derivation of this equation is due to van Laar (1910). Its simplest statistical derivation is based on a treatment suggested by Heitler (1926). The increase in free energy of the system when it is formed at constant temperature and volume is

$$\Delta A = A - (A_1 + A_2), \qquad \dots\dots134$$

where A_1 is the free energy of N_1 molecules of the first kind, and A_2 that of N_2 molecules of the second kind treated as pure components. Hence

$$\Delta A = N_1 kT \ln\left(\frac{N_1}{N_1+N_2}\right) + N_2 kT \ln\left(\frac{N_2}{N_1+N_2}\right) + \left(\frac{N_1 N_2}{N_1+N_2}\right)\Delta u^o. \quad \dots135$$

The gain in free energy of the system when one gram-mole is formed from its components is found by substituting N_o for $N_1 + N_2$. It is

$$\Delta A = x_1 RT \ln x_1 + x_2 RT \ln_2 x_2 + x_1 x_2 \Delta U^o, \qquad \dots\dots136$$

where x is the molar fraction, $R = N_o k$ and $\Delta U^o = N_o \Delta u^o$. The interchange energy is usually regarded as a function of the volume only, so that the gain in total energy on forming one gram-mole of the system is

$$\Delta E = x_1 x_2 \Delta U^o. \qquad \dots\dots137$$

The gain in entropy on forming one gram-mole of solution is thus

$$\Delta S = -R(x_1 \ln x_1 + x_2 \ln x_2), \qquad \dots\dots138$$

which is precisely the expression for the entropy of mixing of two ideal gases or liquids. The term regular was introduced by Hildebrand (1929) to denote all solutions for which the entropy of mixing is given by this equation. When we subtract from equations 136 and 137 the contributions anticipated for ideal systems, we have for the so-called excess thermodynamic functions

$$\Delta A^{ex} = \Delta E = x_1 x_2 \Delta U^o \qquad \dots\dots139$$

and
$$\Delta S^{ex} = 0. \qquad \dots\dots140$$

The increase in the Gibbs free energy ΔG attending the formation of one gram-mole of solution at a constant pressure can be measured from an analysis of the vapour phase with which the solution is at equilibrium, and the increase in heat content ΔH can be measured calorimetrically. A correction first formulated by Scatchard (1937) must be applied before the theory can be tested. Values of ΔG are now available for many binary systems, sometimes at numerous temperatures, but there are very few calorimetric values of ΔH. Fig. 19 shows a specimen set of results obtained with three systems composed of fairly simple molecules. For each system, the quantities ΔG^{ex} and ΔH vary symmetrically with respect to the composition expressed as molar fractions, but they are unequal, indicating that the excess entropy of mixing is not zero. Except in the methyl iodide-chloroform system, however, the observed entropy of mixing, corrected to what it would have been if the mixing occurred at constant volume, differs by not more than 1 per cent. from the ideal value. The present theory of regular solutions thus provides an excellent first approximation to the behaviour of certain real solutions. This has proved to be true even when the ratio of the molar volumes of the components is far from unity, and when the intermolecular forces are far from spherical symmetry.

Ideal solutions are those for which ΔU^o is zero. Positive or negative departures from Raoult's law are seen to correspond to positive or negative values of the interchange energy. Separation into two phases clearly occurs at the consolute temperature $\Delta U^o/2R$. The partial vapour pressure of a component in a regular solution is related as follows to its molar fraction in solution and to its vapour pressure p^o in the pure state

$$p_1 = p_1^o x_1 e^{(1-x_1)^2 \Delta u^o/kT}. \qquad \ldots\ldots\ldots 141$$

The total pressure of the system is

$$P = p_1 + p_2 = p_1^o x_1 e^{(1-x_1)^2 \Delta u^o/kT} + p_2^o x_2 e^{(1-x_2)^2 \Delta u^o/kT}, \qquad \ldots\ldots\ldots 142$$

which reduces to equation 123 when Δu^o is zero. The effect of moderate pressure on the size of the molecules can be ignored, and the osmotic pressure of a regular solution is then given by the equation:

$$\Pi = \frac{kT}{v_1}[-\ln x_1 - (1-x_1)^2(\Delta u^o/kT)], \qquad \ldots\ldots\ldots 143$$

where v_1 is the molecular volume of the solvent. On combining these equations, we obtain a result which is earlier, more general, and independent of the assumption of regularity:

$$\Pi = \frac{kT}{v_1}\ln\frac{p_1^o}{p_1}. \qquad \ldots\ldots\ldots 144$$

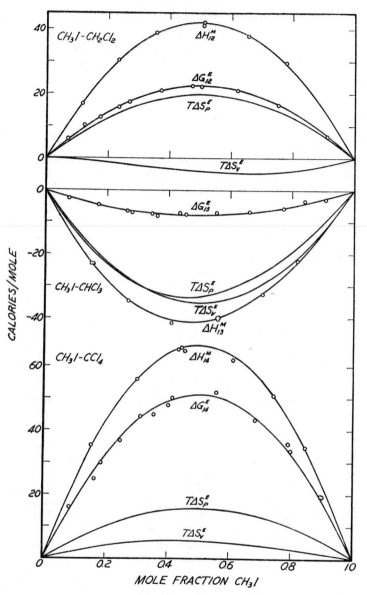

Fig. 19. Excess thermodynamic functions CH₃l-chloromethanes at 25° C. The subscripts ₂, ₃ and ₄ denote, respectively, methylene dichloride CH_2Cl_2, chloroform $CHCl_3$, and carbon tetrachloride CCl_4 (Moelwyn-Hughes and Missen, 1957).

This relation between the osmotic pressure of a solution and the partial pressure of the solvent (Arrhenius, 1889) reduces to van't Hoff's equation for solutions of relatively low concentrations.

The viscosity, the coefficient of diffusion and the freezing point of regular solutions can, like most of their properties, be evaluated in terms of their composition and the ratio $\Delta u^o/kT$.

Irregular solutions

The theory of regular solutions has been, on the whole, so successful that several modifications of it have not unnaturally appeared. A strict statistical theory of solutions is hardly possible when the molecules forming it have different shapes and sizes, and exert forces which are not spherically symmetrical. The problem becomes less intractable when the ratio of the molar volumes of the two components is integral. In such a case, the most probable arrangement of molecules in an imaginary lattice framework may be calculated, allowing each of the larger molecules to occupy an integral number, r, of contiguous sites. Solutions of high polymers, such as those of rubber and polystyrene in benzene lend themselves well to this treatment, which has been quantitatively formulated by Flory (1941), Huggins (1941), Miller (1943) and Guggenheim (1944) and found to be in agreement with the experimental findings of Gee (1942) and Baughan (1948). Miller, for example, derives the following expression for the osmotic pressure of a solution containing n_2 molecules of polymer per c.c. of solution:

$$\Pi = \frac{kT}{v_1}\left\{-\ln_e(1-n_2v_2)+\frac{c}{2}\ln_e\left[1-\frac{2}{c}\left(1-\frac{1}{r}\right)n_2v_2\right]\right\}\quad\ldots\ldots\ldots 145$$

where v_1 is the molecular volume of the monomer and c its co-ordination number. v_2 is the molecular volume of the polymer, and r the number of units of monomer in one polymer molecule. A treatment of binary solutions formed of molecules whose volume ratio is not necessarily integral (Moelwyn-Hughes, 1951) affords the following expression for the osmotic pressure:

$$\Pi = \frac{kT}{v_1}\left[-\ln_e(1-n_2v_2)-n_2(v_2-v_1)-n_2^2v_2\sqrt{v_1v_2}\cdot\frac{\Delta u^o}{kT}\right].\quad\ldots\ldots 146$$

The data for aqueous solutions of sucrose at $0°$ C. are accurately reproduced by this equation, with $\Delta u^o/kT = 1\cdot412$ and $v_2/v_1 = 11\cdot32$.

Prior to these advances, and responsible in large measure for them, came the valuable suggestion by Scatchard (1931) that, in computing the interaction energy of a molecule with those surrounding

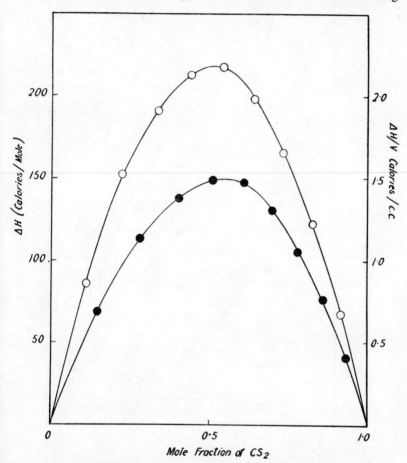

FIG. 20. Increases in heat content attending the formation of one gram-mole of carbon disulphide-chloroform mixtures at 290° K.

Lower curve: ΔH plotted against Molar fraction of CS_2
Upper curve: $\Delta H/V$ plotted against Volume fraction of CS_2

it in solution, the significant terms are the volume fractions rather than the molar fractions of its components. Coupled with the assumption that ϕ_{12} may be taken as the geometric mean of ϕ_{11} and ϕ_{22} the hypothesis enabled him to show that the increase in

F

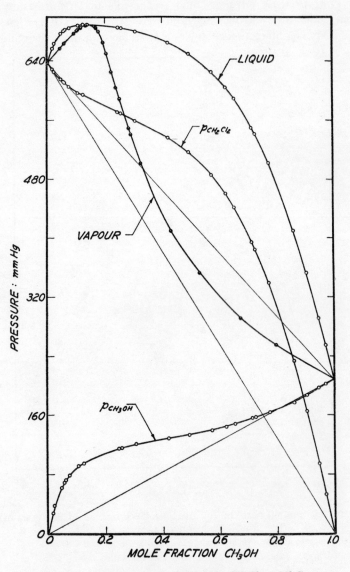

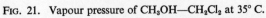

Fig. 21. Vapour pressure of CH_3OH—CH_2Cl_2 at 35° C.

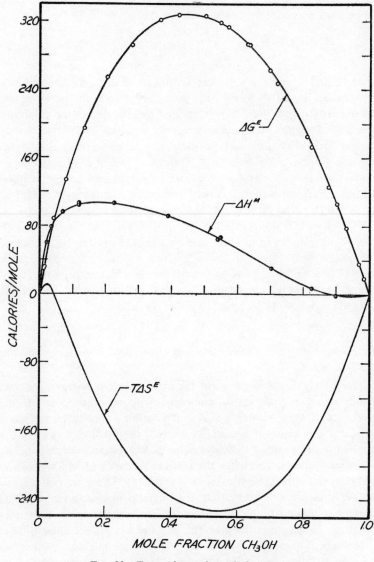

FIG. 22. Excess thermodynamic functions
CH_3OH—CCl_4 at 35° C.

energy of a solution when one gram-mole is formed from its pure components at a constant molar volume V is

$$\frac{\Delta E}{V} = \theta_1 \theta_2 \left[\left(\frac{L_1}{V_1} \right)^{\frac{1}{2}} - \left(\frac{L_2}{V_2} \right)^{\frac{1}{2}} \right]^2, \qquad \ldots\ldots\ldots 147$$

where θ_1 and θ_2 are the volume fractions, L_1 and L_2 the molar heats of vaporisation and V_1 and V_2 the molar volumes of the pure liquids. The quantity within the brackets, termed by Hildebrand the solubility parameter, becomes zero when the energy densities of the two liquids are identical. For such liquids, there should be no heat of mixing. For real values of the solubility parameter, the heat of mixing per unit volume should vary symmetrically with respect to the volume fraction. This conclusion has been verified in a number of instances, one of which is the carbon disulphide-chloroform system (Fig. 20).

Deviations from regularity have, however, been found which differ in magnitude from what can be attributed to the inequality of energy densities. Figs. 21 and 22, which are to be compared with Figs. 17 and 19, show how very different the chlormethane-methanol systems are from the chlormethane-methyl iodide systems. Alcoholic and hydroxylic solutions generally await elucidation.

The evaluation of intermolecular energy constants from the properties of solution

In principle, a knowledge of the intermolecular energy constants of the separate components combined with accurate data on the properties of their solutions makes it possible to evaluate the intermolecular constants of the unlike pairs. In practice, however, the problem is an extremely difficult one, even for systems with spherically symmetrical forces, and when the integers m and n of Mie's equation are taken to be the same for ϕ_{11}, ϕ_{22} and ϕ_{12}. There are two reasons for the difficulty. One is that legitimate comparison of potential energies is limited to the absolute zero of temperature. The other is that, in the nature of the problem, ϕ_{11} and ϕ_{22} cannot differ widely; if they did, it would be false to assume random mixing. Such comparisons as have been made have been based on experimental values of the molar volumes of the pure components and of their partial molar volumes at infinite dilution. They indicate that ϕ_{12} is usually intermediate between ϕ_{11} and ϕ_{22} and is nearer to their arithmetic than to their geometric mean.

VII

THE IONIC STATE

WHEN common salt dissolves in water, there is a slight absorption of heat, giving little evidence of the enormous heat changes, of opposite sign, which have in fact taken place. The contraction in volume gives a more significant clue, for its magnitude is such as would require, in the absence of the salt, an external pressure of about 1000 atmospheres. The colour effects attending the dissolution of some salts provide some indication of what is happening. Anhydrous cupric sulphate, which is colourless in the crystalline state, gives a sky-blue solution on dissolving in water, and an intense blue solution in aqueous ammonia. Arrhenius (1887) suggested that such salts, on dissolving in polar solvents like water and ammonia, dissociate into ions, such as Na^+ and Cl^- in the case of NaCl, and Cu^{++} and SO_4^{--} in the case of $CuSO_4$. His view was hotly contested, chiefly by those who failed to realise that the properties of ions in solution differ widely except in their electrical charges, from the properties of gaseous ions. Ions in solution are, as we now know, attached to solvent molecules of sufficient number to protect them from the rapid recombination which characterises the unprotected ions in gases. The positive ions in aqueous ammoniacal solutions of cupric salts, for example, are tetrahedral structures such as

$$\left[\begin{array}{c} H_2 \\ O \\ | \\ H_2O-Cu-OH_2 \\ | \\ O \\ H_2 \end{array} \right]^{++} \quad \text{and} \quad \left[\begin{array}{c} H_3 \\ N \\ | \\ H_3N-Cu-NH_3 \\ | \\ N \\ H_3 \end{array} \right]^{++},$$

with other solvated ions of intermediate composition. That the co-ordination number is 4 has long been established in one of the simplest experiments of physical chemistry. The theory of Arrhenius, though no longer in dispute, requires extension, and a quantitative treatment.

Limiting laws

Experiments with non-electrolytes show that the osmotic pressure of solutions and the lowering in the freezing points of solvents are determined by the concentration of solute molecules. The magnitude of these properties, reckoned per gram-mole of solute, is greater for electrolytes than for non-electrolytes by factors which tend, at infinite dilution, to integers, such as 2 for sodium chloride, 3 for barium chloride, and so on. At infinite dilution, therefore, electrolytes behave as if they were completely ionised and the ions contribute independently and additively to the observable properties of the solutions. In dilute solutions, which may here be regarded as those containing about 1 millimole of electrolyte per litre, departures from these rules of independence are observed, and their extent is often linearly related to the square-root of the concentration, c.

The first square-root law discovered relates to the equivalent conductivity, Λ, and may be expressed as follows:

$$\Lambda = \Lambda^o - A\sqrt{c}, \qquad \qquad \dots\dots\dots 148$$

where A is a constant. Established by Kohlransch (1900) with aqueous solutions of the nitrates and halides of some of the alkali metals, it has been confirmed, by Walden and others, with different values of A, for many other salts and solvents. The second property, found (by Mellanby, 1905) to vary as the square-root of the concentration is the logarithm of the ionic activity coefficient, γ_i, which is defined in terms of the chemical potential μ_i and the ionic concentration, c_i, by the empirical equation

$$\mu_i = \mu_i^o + kT \ln c_i + kT \ln \gamma_i. \qquad \qquad \dots\dots\dots 149$$

Among other properties which obey a square-root law in dilute solutions are the heat of dissolution, the osmotic pressure and the coefficient of diffusion.

One cause of the difference in properties between a solution containing ions (N_i of one kind, N_j of another kind, and so on) and a solution containing the same number of uncharged particles in the same volume V must be due to the Coulombic interactions of the ions. When these are summed over all possible pairs, there results the following expression for the electrostatic component of the free energy of the solution:

$$A_e = \Sigma \frac{N_i e_i^2}{2Dr_i} - \frac{V \kappa^3 kT}{12\pi}. \qquad \qquad \dots\dots\dots 150$$

Here e_i is the ionic charge, r_i the ionic " radius," and D is the uniform dielectric constant of the solvent at temperature T. The reciprocal distance κ is defined by the equation $\kappa^2 = 4\pi \Sigma N_i e_i^2 / DkTV$. This conclusion is due to S. R. Milner (1913) whose treatment, however, led to a slight numerical error which was avoided in the simpler and more direct derivation given by Debye and Hückel (1923). The electrostatic component of the chemical potential is

$$\mu_i^e = \left(\frac{\partial A_e}{\partial N_i}\right)_{T,V,N_j\dots} = \frac{e_i^2}{2Dr_i} - \frac{e_i^2 \kappa}{2D}. \qquad \dots\dots151$$

Since the ions at infinite dilution obey van't Hoff's laws, we can write for the chemical potential in dilute solutions

$$\mu_i = \mu_i^o + kT \ln c_i - \frac{e_i^2 \kappa}{2D}, \qquad \dots\dots152$$

which gives an immediate interpretation to Mellanby's law, and to its extension by G. N. Lewis and Linhart (1919). The heat content and most other properties of a system depend upon its free energy; the empirical square-root laws can thus be explained, since κ, by definition, is proportional to $\sqrt{c}$.

To interpret Kohlrausch's law, allowance must be made for the fact that the motion of an ion in an externally applied electrical field is influenced by the tendency of the cloud surrounding it to move in the opposite direction (the electrophoretic effect), and by the distortion of the charge distribution from the spherical symmetry prevailing in the absence of the external field (the relaxation effect). Both these effects have been shown by Debye and Hückel to vary as $\sqrt{c}$. With an additional correction introduced by Onsager (1926) to allow for the effect of Brownian motion, it becomes possible to evaluate A/Λ^o in terms of independently measured qualities. The absolute evaluation of Λ^o has still to be made.

In view of the fact that these square-root laws are seldom obeyed by solutions containing more than 1 millimole of electrolyte per litre, there is some force, if little charity, in the comment that the Milner-Debye theory is less one of electrolytic solutions than of slightly polluted solvents. At any rate, it has been so extensively described as to need no further elaboration here, where we are more concerned with the determination, in absolute magnitude, of some of the properties of ions at infinite dilution, and with such attempts as have been made to account for the behaviour of electrolytic solutions over the whole range of their composition.

The heats of escape of ions from solution

When from the lattice energy of a salt (Table 4) is subtracted the relatively small gain in energy attending its dissolution, we obtain the energy required to liberate the ions from solution. The data for some of the alkali halides in water, when arranged as in Table 8, show that each ion contributes independently to the heat of escape. Otherwise it would be difficult to explain the following constant differences between the heats of escape of pairs of salts containing a common ion:

$$Li^+ - Na^+ = 26 \cdot 2 \pm 0 \cdot 5 \ . \ F^- - Cl^- = 32 \cdot 9 \pm 0 \cdot 7$$
$$Na^+ - K^+ = 20 \cdot 0 \pm 0 \cdot 3 \ . \ Cl^- - Br^- = 8 \cdot 0 \pm 0 \cdot 2$$
$$K^+ - Rb^+ = 6 \cdot 2 \pm 0 \cdot 5 \ . \ Br^- - I^- = 8 \cdot 9 \pm 0 \cdot 5.$$

TABLE 8

Heats of escape (in kilocalories per gram-mole) of the ions of alkali halides from aqueous solution at 298·16° K

	F	Cl	Br	I
Li	244·9	211·3	203·5	194·7
	(244·2)	(211·3)	(203·5)	(194·4)
Na	218·2	185·6	177·6	168·3
	(218·0)	(185·1)	(177·1)	(168·2)
K	197·9	165·5	157·7	148·5
	(198·0)	(165·1)	(157·1)	(148·2)
Rb	192·1	159·2	150·9	142·6
	(191·8)	(158·9)	(150·9)	(142·0)

There is, however, no absolute method of determining the proportion into which the total heat of escape must be shared. Many guesses have been made. Among them, the potassium and fluoride ions may be allocated equal parts (Fajans, 1928). On this assumption, we find the ionic heats of escape to be as follows:

Li^+	145·2	F^-	99·0
Na^+	119·0	Cl^-	66·1
K^+	99·0	Br^-	58·1
Rb^+	92·8	I^-	49·2.

The bracketed values of Table 8 show how well these reproduce the results. By a similar argument, basing our knowledge on the heats of dissolution of the hydrogen halides, and the energies required to ionise the gaseous molecules, a mean value of 243 ± 2 kilocalories is found for the heat of escape of the hydrogen ion. If we subtract from this very large term the proton affinity of the water molecule, which has been estimated as 169 ± 2 kilocalories, we are left with a figure of 75 ± 4 for the heat of escape of the proton monohydrate H_3O^+ from an aqueous solution at $25°$ C.

Born's theory

To explain these quantities, Born (1920) considered the energy required for the reversible charging of N_i independent ions of charge e_i and radius r_i at constant temperature and pressure in a solvent of dielectric constant, D. Electrostatic theory provides the expression:

$$G^e = \frac{N_i e_i^2}{2Dr_i}, \qquad \dots\dots\dots 153$$

as indicated in equation 150. To obtain the component of the heat content arising from the electrical charge, we employ the Kelvin-Helmholtz equation, using the empirical expression of Abegg (1897) for the dielectric constant, as generalised by Lowry and Jessop (1930): $L = L_o e^{-LT}$. Then

$$H^e = \frac{N_i e_i^2}{2Dr_i}(1 - LT). \qquad \dots\dots\dots 154$$

The gain in heat content when the ions are transferred from solution to a vacuum is thus

$$\Delta H^e = \frac{N_i e_i^2}{2r_i}\left[1 - \left(\frac{1-LT}{D}\right)\right]. \qquad \dots\dots\dots 155$$

After inserting numerical constants for water at $25°$ C., and expressing r_i in Angstrom units, we obtain, in kilocalories per gram-ion, the expression

$$\Delta H^e = 166/\overset{o}{r_i}. \qquad \dots\dots\dots 155a$$

Qualitatively, this result is not unsatisfactory. The heats of escape of small ions exceed those of large ions. Quantitatively, it has many drawbacks, as Gatty, Wolfenden and others (1934) have pointed out.

There have been numerous attempts to reconcile the calorimetric values of ΔH^e with the crystal " radii ", r_c, as given by Goldschmidt. To obtain a linear plot using the data for elementary univalent ions, it has been found necessary (Latimer, Pitzer and Slansky, 1939) to add empirical increments of $0\cdot 1$ Å to the cationic and $0\cdot 85$ Å to the anionic radii.

The gain in entropy due to the reversible charging is found, from equation 153, to be

$$S^e = -\frac{N_i e_i^2 L}{2Dr_i}. \qquad \ldots\ldots\ldots 156$$

The principal drawback to Born's theory is the assumption that the solvent is a continuous medium, with a uniform dielectric constant up to the boundary of the ion. In a satisfactory theory the molecular structure of the solvent must be taken into account, as Bernal and Fowler (1933) and Verwey (1941) have pointed out. In most modifications of the original theory, significant energy terms are introduced to allow for the change in structure of the solvent, but equation 153 is nevertheless retained as the principal component of the free energy of ions in solution.

Ionic solvation in terms of intermolecular forces

An alternative approach to the problem can be made, without appealing to the concepts of ionic radii or dielectric constant, by considering the forces exerted between an ion and the c solvent molecules which are assumed to surround it symmetrically. If the additional repulsions between solvent molecules thus radially situated, and the energies of induction are ignored, the principal electrostatic energy of the solvated ion is $c(Aa^{-n} - |z| \varepsilon\mu a^{-2})$ where a is the distance between the centres of the ion and the solvent molecule. The first term is the energy of intrinsic repulsion between the ion and the c solvent molecules; the second term is the energy of attraction between the ion, of valency $|z|$ and the solvent molecules each with a dipole moment μ. The electrostatic contribution to the free energy of a solution containing N_i ions, each at its equilibrium distance a_o is

$$G_e = -N_i c |z| \varepsilon\mu \left(1 - \frac{2}{n}\right) a_o^{-2}. \qquad \ldots\ldots\ldots 157$$

It is to be observed that G_e is always negative. According to this treatment (Moelwyn-Hughes, 1948), the electrostatic contribution to ionic entropy,

$$S_e = N_i c \, |z| \, \varepsilon\mu \left(1 - \frac{2}{n}\right) a_o^{-2} \left[\left(\frac{dc}{dT}\right)_P - \frac{2}{a_o}\left(\frac{da_o}{dT}\right)_P\right], \quad \ldots\ldots\ldots 158$$

may, in principle, be positive or negative, and owes its origin to the variation, with respect to temperature, of the co-ordination number c and the ion-solvent separation, a_o. Of these two possible effects, the latter is certainly the more important, as may be judged from such evidence as we have on the temperature variation of the partial molar volumes of ions at infinite dilution. If the term in the square bracket in equation 158 does not vary much from ion to ion, we may expect the electro-static contribution to ionic entropy to vary in proportion to the ionic charge, and in inverse proportion to the square of the ion-solvent distance. The more recent reviews of the data (Powell, 1954) do, in fact, show that this is approximately true, and that S_e can be expressed as a constant minus $|z|/(r_i + 1 \cdot 3)^2$, where r_i is the crystal " radius " in Angstrom units. This experimental fact is to be contrasted with equation 156, according to which S_e is always negative, and should vary as the square of the ionic charge, and inversely as the ionic " radius ". If, instead of eliminating the constants A, we adopt the values afforded by the second virial coefficients of gases or by Born's theory of ionic crystals, it is possible to compute absolute values of a_o and ΔH_e. These are found to be reasonable, and their trends logical. The theory, moreover, explains the difference in the heats of hydration of ions of opposite valency but of the same size.

According to either theory, the hydrogen ion appears as an anomalous entity. It is, perhaps, best regarded as the highly stable monohydrate, H_3O^+, which responds to its four immediate neighbours in the same way as the unhydrated ions Li^+ and F^-.

Ionic activity coefficients in concentrated solutions of electrolytes

The ionic activity coefficients γ which have received most attention have been defined by equations of the same form as equation 149, but with the concentration, c, replaced by the molality m, where m is the number of gram moles of solute in 1000 grams of solvent:

$$\mu_+ = \mu_+^o + kT \ln m_+ + kT \ln \gamma_+,$$

$$\mu_- = \mu_-^o + kT \ln m_- + kT \ln \gamma_-.$$

For a completely ionised uni-univalent electrolyte, $m_+ = m_- = m$, and, if the geometric mean activity coefficient is denoted by γ_2, we have

$$\mu_2 = \mu_+ + \mu_- = \mu_2^o + 2kT \ln m + 2kT \ln \gamma_2. \qquad \ldots\ldots\ldots 159$$

The most accurate method for determining γ_2 for salts in aqueous solution is an indirect one: the activity of the solvent a_1 is measured from its vapour pressure, and the Gibbs-Duhem equation is applied to evaluate γ_2 from it. Experiments show that γ_2, which by definition is unity at zero molality, decreases as m is increased, and passes through a minimum. At high concentrations it exceeds 1, sometimes by factors of about 100.

The most successful attempt to interpret these facts is that of Robinson and Stokes (1948) who have applied to electrolyte solutions the same idea as was used by Poynting and Callendar, i.e. the permanent fixation of n molecules of solvent by the ions, of number v, into which each molecule ionises. After incorporating the rational definition of activity as defined by Scatchard (1925), their expression for the mean activity coefficient of an electrolyte in aqueous solution at 25° C. becomes:

$$\log_{10} \gamma_2 = \frac{0.5092\, z_A z_B \sqrt{c}}{1 + 0.3286 \mathring{a} \sqrt{c}} - \log_{10}[1 - 0.018(n - v)m] - (n/v) \log_{10} a_1.$$

$$\ldots\ldots\ldots 160$$

c is the concentration of electrolyte, in moles per litre of solution: z_A and z_B are the valencies of the ions. The numerator in the first term, which is necessarily negative, is that provided by the limiting expression of the Debye-Hückel theory. The term in the denominator allows for the fact that the ions cannot approach to within a distance less than $\mathring{a}$ (Angstroms) from each other. By fitting this equation to the data, Robinson and Stokes find values of $\mathring{a}$ and n which are, on the whole, reasonable, e.g. $n = 4$, 5 or 6 for a number of univalent elementary cations and anions. The assumption that n is independent of concentration is an admitted over-simplification, but it is a step which has extended the concentration range over which theory can be applied from 1 millimole per litre to about 5 moles per litre.

The total electrostatic energy of concentrated electrolyte solutions

It is a matter of interest to discover what fraction of the total interaction energy of a concentrated aqueous solution can be attributed to the interactions of the ions with the neighbouring water molecules.

To do so, we shall examine the saturated solution of ammonium chloride in water at 25° C. Its composition corresponds to NH_4Cl, 7·54 H_2O. The partial molar volume of the salt in water increases from 37·70 c.c. at infinite dilution to 40·94 c.c. in the saturated solution. Thus the volume occupied by one mole of salt in solution is never very different from the volume of two moles of water. The energy (in kilocalories) required to convert the saturated solution containing one gram-mole of salt into gaseous ions and water molecules is obtained by adding the following 3 calorimetric data:

NH_4Cl (cr.)$\rightarrow NH_4^+$(g.)$+Cl^-$ (g.)   ; $\Delta H_1 = 151$

NH_4^+ (aq.)$+Cl^-$ (aq.)$+7\cdot54$ H_2O (aq.)
$\quad\rightarrow NH_4Cl$ (cr.)$+7\cdot54$ H_2O (liq.)   ; $\Delta H_2 = -4$

$7\cdot54$ H_2O (liq.)$\rightarrow 7\cdot54$ H_2O (g.)   ; $\Delta H_3 = 81$

NH_4^+ (aq.)$+Cl^-$ (aq.)$+7\cdot54$ H_2O (aq.)
$\quad\rightarrow NH_4^+$ (g.)$+Cl^-$ (g.)$+7\cdot54$ H_2O (g.)   ; $\Delta H = 228$.

The calculation requires, in the first place, a knowledge of the structure of the saturated solution. The assumption we shall make is that the ammonium and chloride ions arrange themselves, on an average, in the caesium-chloride type lattice assumed by the crystalline salt with which the solution is at equilibrium. Each ion is thus symmetrically surrounded by eight ions of opposite sign at a distance apart of 5·74 Å. If a water molecule lies midway between the cation and its neighbouring anion, with its polar axis on the interionic line, the average distance between ion and dipole becomes 2·86 Å, and the composition would be NH_4Cl, 8H_2O. We shall take the experimental co-ordination number c to be 7·54 rather than 8, and the repulsion integer of equation 1 to be 9. The energy of interaction of an ion of charge ε with c solvent molecules (of polarisability α and electric moment μ) at a distance a_o apart is then:

$$u = -c\left[\frac{5\alpha\varepsilon^2}{18a_o^4} + \frac{7\varepsilon\mu}{9a_o^2}\right]. \qquad\ldots\ldots\ldots 161$$

The ion-dipole energy for an aqueous solution containing one mole of salt is then found to be -210 kilocalories, leaving a quantity -17 to be ascribed to ion-ion interactions. With the appropriate Madelung constant, this indicates an effective dielectric constant of about 5. More detailed calculations include 4 further terms in u, but they largely cancel out one another's effect.

VIII

THE INTERFACIAL STATE

OF the many interesting aspects of surface chemistry, we shall, in conformity with the object of this book, select those which lend themselves most directly to the general treatment of intermolecular forces. Great advances in the study of interfaces followed the simple interpretation of adsorption given in terms of chemical kinetics by Langmuir (1916). According to it, the number, N_a, of gas molecules of mass m, adsorbed at a temperature T and pressure p on an area O of a plane solid surface containing N_s sites per cm.[2] is given by the equation

$$\frac{O}{N_a} = \frac{O}{N_s} + (2\pi mkT)^{\frac{1}{2}} v \cdot e^{-\psi/kT} \left(\frac{1}{p}\right), \qquad \ldots\ldots\ldots 162$$

where ψ is the energy required by an adsorbed molecule to detach itself from the surface, and v is the probability per second that it becomes detached. At infinite pressure, $N_a = N_{s_t}$, that is, one molecule of gas is adsorbed on each site on the surface of the adsorbent. Our task is to evaluate ψ, which is known to depend on specific properties of the adsorbent and of the adsorbed molecules. It is, for example, 1·6 kilocalories per mole for argon adsorbed on potassium chloride, and 8·0 for ammonia adsorbed on charcoal. The problem at its simplest can be dealt with when the adsorbed molecules are so far apart as not to influence one another. Under such conditions, which correspond to low pressures, ψ is independent of the fraction of the surface covered.

Calculation of the heat of desorption

Let us suppose that the energy of interaction between one molecule of the gas that is to be adsorbed and one molecule of the substance forming the adsorbent is given by equation 1. On integrating all the interactions between a single molecule of the gas, situated at a height

d above a plane surface containing n_a molecules per c.c., and all the molecules in the adsorbent, the total energy of interaction is found to be

$$\Phi = 2\pi n_\alpha \left[\frac{A}{(n-2)(n-3)} \cdot \frac{1}{d^{n-3}} - \frac{B}{(m-2)(m-3)} \frac{1}{d^{m-3}} \right]. \quad \ldots 163$$

If we ignore the repulsion, and take m to be 6, we have

$$-\Phi = \frac{\pi n_\alpha B}{6d^3}. \quad \ldots\ldots\ldots 164$$

This equation was applied by London (1930) to evaluate the heat of desorption of various gases and vapours from charcoal. The maximum gain in energy due to the desorption of a single molecule from a plane bare surface is

$$\lambda_o = -\Phi_o = \frac{2\pi n_\alpha B}{(m-2)d_o^{m-3}} \left[\frac{1}{m-3} - \frac{1}{n-3} \right], \quad \ldots\ldots\ldots 165$$

where the nearest distance to the surface is given by the equation

$$d_o^{n-m} = \frac{(m-2)A}{(n-2)B}. \quad \ldots\ldots\ldots 166$$

With $m = 6$ and $n = 9$, it follows that

$$\lambda_o = -\Phi_o = \frac{\pi n_\alpha B}{12d_o^3}, \quad \ldots\ldots\ldots 167$$

which is one-half of the value found when no allowance is made for repulsions. By expanding the expression for $\Phi - \Phi_o$, it is found that, for small values of $d - d_o$, the motion of the adsorbed atom, of mass μ, perpendicular to the surface, is a harmonic vibration with a frequency

$$v = \frac{1}{2\pi d_o} \left[\frac{(m-3)(n-3)}{\mu} \right]^{\frac{1}{2}}. \quad \ldots\ldots\ldots 168$$

If the adsorbed molecule lies in the plane of the surface, but over a hemispherical cavity, the heat of desorption is

$$\lambda_o = -\Phi_o = \frac{2\pi n_\alpha B}{d_o^{m-3}} \left[\frac{1}{m-3} - \frac{1}{n-3} \right], \quad \ldots\ldots\ldots 169$$

which is greater than the heat of desorption from a perfectly planar surface. This explains why molecules tend to be adsorbed first in the cracks of an otherwise plane surface.

Cohesion

The procedure of the last section can be directly extended to the determination of the total energy of interaction between two phases, containing molecular concentrations n_α and n_β, and contacting in a plane surface of area O cm.[2]. The result is

$$-U_o = \frac{2\pi(n-m)n_\alpha n_\beta B_{\alpha\beta} O}{(m-2)(m-3)(m-4)(n-4)d_o^{m-4}} = b_{\alpha\beta}n_\alpha n_\beta O. \quad \ldots 170$$

The gain in energy when such an interface is made from the pure phases is

$$U_\sigma = (b_\alpha n_\alpha^2 + b_\beta n_\beta^2 - 2b_{\alpha\beta}n_\alpha n_\beta)O. \qquad \ldots\ldots\ldots 171$$

If the two phases consist of the same chemical species, the b terms are identical, and the surface energy per unit area is

$$U_\sigma/O = (n_\alpha - n_\beta)^2 b. \qquad \ldots\ldots\ldots 172$$

This quantity becomes zero under critical conditions. Equations of this form have been derived by Fowler (1937) and Wheeler (1938).

Surface tension

A good estimate of the surface tension of a liquid may be obtained by regarding n_β as the molecular concentration of the vapour, and n_α that of the liquid. When the former can be neglected in comparison with the latter, we have, when $m = 6$ and $n = 9$,

$$\frac{U_\sigma}{O} = \frac{\pi n_\alpha^2 B}{20 d_o^2} \qquad \ldots\ldots\ldots 173$$

Applied to liquid mercury at $0°$ C., U_o/O becomes 344 ergs/cm.[2], which is about 70 per cent. of the observed total free energy per unit surface. Jura (1948), using Hildebrand's distribution function for molecules in the surface, obtained a value considerably nearer the experimental surface tension. The incorporation of equation 1 into the equation of state for monolayers, derived by Mitchell (1935), provides a satisfactory interpretation of the Eötvös equation.

Stefan's ratio

The ratio of the surface energy E_σ per molecule of liquid to its heat of vaporisation L_s when both are extrapolated to the absolute zero of temperature is approximately 0·432 for argon, mercury, hydrogen and nitrous oxide; 0·338 for nitrogen, carbon monoxide and carbon disulphide; and 0·261 for carbon tetrachloride and benzene. The simplest interpretation of these values is that given by Wolf and Klapproth (1940). If the value of ϕ in the liquid and surface phases is the same, but the co-ordination numbers c_L and c_σ different, then

$$\frac{E_\sigma}{L_s} = 1 - \frac{c_\sigma}{c_L}. \qquad \dots\dots\dots 174$$

The co-ordination number of a molecule on the liquid surface of a face-centred arrangement of molecules may thus be 7, 8 or 9. It has also been shown that Stefan's ratio for liquids which obey Mie's potential depends entirely on the integers in his equation, and is

$$\frac{E_\sigma}{L_s} = \frac{(n-3)}{(m-2)(m-4)(n-4)} \left[\frac{(n-2)(n-3)}{(m-2)(m-3)}\right]^{\frac{m-3}{n-m}}. \qquad \dots 175$$

Van der Waals forces, and direct confirmation of their nature

Much confusion has arisen concerning the term " van der Waals forces ", due in part to the incomplete form in which his empirical equation is usually written, and in part to a failure to appreciate the assumptions which enabled London to reconcile the empirical constants of the van der Waals equation with those of intermolecular force theory.

Van der Waals (1873) represented the pressure P exerted by N molecules of a fluid occupying a volume V at temperature T in terms of these variables and of two empirical constants which are here denoted by σ and Z (*cf.* equation 60):

$$P = \frac{NkT}{V-(\frac{2}{3})\pi N\sigma^3} - \frac{N^2Z}{V^2}. \qquad \dots\dots\dots 176$$

In terms of the average volume per molecule ($v = N/V$), we can write

$$P = \frac{kT}{v-(\frac{2}{3})\pi\sigma^3} - \frac{Z}{v^2}. \qquad \dots\dots\dots 177$$

The critical constants of the fluid are readily shown to be $v_c = 2\pi\sigma^3$; $P_c = Z/3(2\pi\sigma^3)^2$; and $kT_c = 4Z/9\pi\sigma^3$. It is with the last term of equation 177, which represents the statical pressure, P_s, that we are here concerned. It denotes an average intermolecular force X varying inversely as the fourth power of the average intermolecular distance, *a*

G

(W. Sutherland, 1886; Partington, 1949). As this conclusion is continually being disputed (e.g. by H. A. Taylor, 1958), the way it is arrived at must be briefly shown. The statical pressure is given in general as

$$P_s = -\frac{dU}{dV} = -\frac{du}{dv},$$ 178

when U and V are the potential energy and volume of the system, and u and v the average molecular potential energy and average molecular volume respectively. Hence

$$P_s = -\frac{du}{da}\cdot\frac{da}{dv} = -\frac{a}{3v}\frac{du}{da} = \frac{a}{3v}X.$$ 179

If we accept van der Waals' expression for P_s, it follows that

$$X = -\frac{3Z}{va},$$ 180

which, since v is directly proportional to a^3, denotes a force varying as a^{-4}. This force law corresponds to a value of $m = 3$ in equation 1, an exponent in the attractive energy term frequently adopted in early explorations of molecular force fields in gases, and not abandoned until London established m as 6 for non-polar molecules. A theoretical interpretation of the empirical constants of the van der Waals equation is made possible, as we have seen in deriving equation 70, by assuming that (1) only the second virial coefficient is relevant, and (2) the real field of force may be replaced by an approximate and discontinuous one, giving infinite repulsion when the average intermolecular distance is equal to or less than σ.

Experimental proof that m is 6 and not 3 has been obtained within recent years by direct measurement of the force of attraction exerted between quartz plates when their distance, d, apart is of the order of magnitude of 100 Å. At greater distances, the attraction forces are diminished by a retardation, as shown by Casimir and Polder (1948). At this separation, however, and at closer distances, the energy of repulsion can be ignored, and the theoretical expression for the total force of attraction per unit area, obtained by integrating equation 3, is

$$\frac{X}{O} = -\frac{2\pi n_\alpha^2 B}{(m-2)(m-3)}\cdot\frac{1}{d^{m-3}},$$ 181

where n_α is the number of molecules per c.c. Within these distances, and with quartz plates free from electrical charges, Black, de Jongh, Overbeck and Sparnaay (1960) find that the force between the plates varies in proportion to $1/d^3$, i.e. $m = 6$. Moreover, the magnitude of the force is adequately given by equation 181, with the theoretical value of B. According to the same theory, the force of attraction between unit area of a flat plate and a sphere should vary as $1/d^2$. This law also has been directly verified (Howe, Benton and Puddington, 1955). There no longer remains any doubt, on theoretical or experimental grounds, that the forces of attraction between isolated pairs of non-polar molecules obey the inverse seventh law.

INDEX OF NAMES

93

INDEX OF SUBJECTS